THE ASSEMBLIES OF AL-HARIRI

Also by Amina Shah

ARABIAN FAIRY TALES (Muller)
FOLK TALES OF CENTRAL ASIA (Octagon)
THE TALE OF THE FOUR DERVISHES (Octagon)

THE ASSEMBLIES OF AL-HARIRI

FIFTY ENCOUNTERS WITH THE SHAYKH ABU ZAYD OF SERUJ

1, 11, 12, 23, 25, 31, 48, 50

retold by
AMINA SHAH

from
The Makamat of Al-Hariri of Basra

THE OCTAGON PRESS
LONDON

Copyright © 1980 by The Octagon Press

**Reprinted by the Octagon Press with the aid of
a subvention from the Sufi Trust**

ISBN 900860 86 3

First Published 1981
Reprinted 1987

Printed and bound in Great Britain by
Redwood Burn Ltd., Trowbridge, Wiltshire

MAY ALL THAT WAS BEST IN THEM
LIVE ON IN US.

NOTE

A number of Hariri's "Assemblies" consist of
sequences of riddles and other forms of play upon
words. Since these cannot be adequately translated
from Arabic, they are accompanied by a series of
explanatory notes.

NOTES ON AL HARIRI OF BASRA

Al Hariri was born in A.D. 1030, A.H.466, and died in his native city in the year A.H.516, in the street of the Beni Harram (a tribe of Bedouin Arabs). He is called in full Abu Mohammed Al Kasmir Ibn Ali Al Hariri, and "Hariri" because he had at one time traded in silk (*harir*) or had a manufactory of it. The family of Hariri belonged to the small village of Mesham near Basra, where he is said to have possessed eighteen thousand palm trees and enjoyed great opulence.

The occasion of undertaking the composition of the Makamat is related by his son Abdullah Abu'l Kasim: "My father was seated one day in the mosque which he usually frequented, when there entered an elderly Shaykh clad in two ragged cloaks, with all the appearance of a destitute wayfarer, but who spoke with great fluency and expressed himself with elegance. When asked by the people present who he was, he said his name was Abu Zayd of Seruj. Astonished at finding one so ragged eloquent in this manner, my father went home and composed the Makamat entitled "of the Mosque Beni Harram". This, when published, was read by the Vizir Abu Nasr Anushirwan, an erudite and talented person, who commissioned my father to write more of the same sort, which he did to the number of fifty."

The name "Zayd" is used by the Arabs to denote "any man whatever", and the name which Hariri gives to the narrator of the tales is Harith Hamman, which translated means . . . *Harith* "one who acquires gain by trade or other means" and *Hamman* "one who is subject to cares and anxieties".

The meaning of the word *Makamat* is derived from "a place where one stands upright" and hence, the place where one is at any time. Next it is used metonymically to denote "the persons assembled at any place" and finally, by another transition, "the discourses delivered or conversations held in any such assembly". This metaphorical use of the word Makamat has however been restricted to discourse and conversations like those narrated by Hariri and his predecessor Al Hamadani, which are composed in a highly finished style, and solely for the purpose of exhibiting specimens of various kinds of eloquence, and exemplifying rules of grammar, rhetoric and poetry. It is never applied to the colloquies of ordinary life, like those narrated in the "Thousand Nights and One Night" for the purpose of mere amusement and not instruction.

The Arabic commentators on Al Hariri are very numerous, the chief of them being Al Sharisi, Al Razi, Al Motarezi and Al Akbari. Al Sharisi is surnamed from his native place Shares (Jerez) in Andalucia. His is the most voluminous commentary which has been written on the *Makamat*. Haji Kalfa, who says that it renders all other commentaries superfluous, places his death at about A.H. 619. His explanations are certainly very clear, complete and valuable, but he is fond of displaying the extent of his own reading, and somewhat encumbers his MS. with a profusion of quotations from many poets, many of which are but remotely connected with the subject of the *Makamat*.

There are many lessons hidden in the picaresque adventures of Shaykh Abu Zayd. Often words from well-known phrases from the Koran are given pride of place by being put into the mouths of the characters in the stories. Often again, some allusion to the workings of fate in our lives and the inevitability of the law of chance, as for instance in the tale of the Arab who found a sheep in the desert, and wishing to kill it for food, had nothing to slaughter it with, till the sheep began to scrape on the ground and uncovered a buried knife. It would appear that in each tale Hariri gives us the chance to wonder if the means reasonably justifies the end. The character of the wily Abu Zayd of Seruj — eloquent and erratic like the hero of the Odyssey — roaming from place to place with no means of support except his marvellous powers of language, nor any object save the display of them, restless if without an opportunity of exerting them, but careless from the very confidence of success about employing them in a settled direction, devoting them sometimes to the noblest and sometimes to the meanest purpose, but applying them to foil the learned and cajole the simple, to baffle the powerful and to defraud the humane (yet never losing sight of the dignity of their possession) — this character provides an amplification of and an improvement on the tales of the Mulla Nasrudin, or Nasrudin Khoja, the clown-wiseman of the Middle East.

We see in the book the human condition as it affects us, sometimes the man on the saddle, sometimes the saddle on the man. Harith Hamman, Abu Zayd's admirer, companion and reporter, who is constantly on the look-out for him, yearning for his wonderful night-talks and poetry, always seems to pay dearly for the pleasure of meeting him; yet, nevertheless can never have enough of him.

By means of the repeated exhibition of these two characters in lively contrast to each other, Hariri has succeeded in maintaining a certain unity in his work, and in avoiding abrupt transitions, while he introduces specimens of all the different species of composition which it was his design to illustrate. By this means he has preserved a graceful dramatic effect and such a pleasing variety as might beguile and encourage his readers to study what he designates as "a combination of serious language with lightsome, refinement with nervousness of style, and elegant with recondite phraseology, a rich store of choice metaphors, and ancient proverbs, and riddles, and orations, and poems, religious, festive, plaintive and didactic."

The work is no idle rhapsody intended like the "Thousand Nights and One Night" to amuse the loiterers of the cafe or the seraglio, but the elaborate result of the literary system of a period in which not only the sciences but the useful arts of life were sacrificed by the ingenious and studious of a great nation to a profound grammatical and rhetorical research into the structure and resources of their own most copious language. If the author has arrayed his production in the garb of anecdote, it is an artifice by which its stateliness might be made less formidable, and its treasures most accessible.

At the time when this book was written, it was not uncommon for destitute strangers to enter the learned circle where the choicest wits of the province were assembled, and, as soon as the opportunity offered itself, compel all to listen to their own special brand of rhetoric, winning their bounty by some remarkable feat of marvellous improvisation, or a lucid decision on some perplexing difficulty in grammar or poetry. Thus it appears that Shaykh Abu Zayd as depicted in the *Makamat* is no more than the **type** to which the then structure of literary society appealed most. The *Makamat* therefore combines the primary excellence of being a grand collection of the literature admired during a long and important period of Moslem supremacy, and the secondary one of containing a correct delineation of one of its most eminent professors.

Every "Assembly" composed by Hariri is but a variation on the same theme. His hero, Abu Zayd, is always the same ill-dressed, crafty old man, full of learning and genius, unscrupulous as to the artifices which he uses to effect his purpose, reckless in

spending in forbidden indulgences the money he has
obtained by his wits or deceit, but with the veins of true
feeling in him.

There is real moral excellence in much of what he
writes; many of his discourses, though put into the
mouth of Abu Zayd, are without blemish. Hariri
depicts favourably the witty and cynical improviser
with his two wives — one old and weather-beaten like
himself, the other a handsome, impudent young jade,
the ready instrument of her husband's knaveries. Abu
Zayd and his family are but the setting for the pearls of
poetry and wisdom which the author lavishes on the
world.

Hariri's chief works, after "The Assemblies", are
two treatises on grammar, one called "The Beauties of
the I'rab" (or desinential system) the other "The Pearl
of the Diver". In this latter Hariri points out the faults
made by people of education in the use of words and
phrases. Every sentence is like a drop of grammatical
gold.

Ibn Khallikan tells us that Hariri was a man of most
unprepossessing appearance, and that when a stranger
came to visit him to discuss one of his books, and
Hariri saw that he was somewhat put out by Hariri's
unattractiveness, he said to him: "I am a man to be
heard, not to be seen."

CONTENTS

"Live by beguiling, for you are in a world (or time)
    whose sons are as the lions of Bisheh,
And turn on the stream of craft, so you may make the
    mill of livelihood go round.
Hunt after the eagle, but if the chase fail, be content if
    you but strike off a feather.
Seek to pluck the fruit, but if that escapes you, be
    satisfied with the leaves.
Ease your heart from distracting care if fortune is
    adverse,
For the changing of events gives notice to man of life's
    uncertainty."

                                        Abu Zayd of Seruj.

THE PREFACE OF AL HARIRI

In the Name of God, the Merciful, most Merciful.

Said the excellent, the incomparable, Abu Mohammed al Kasim ibn Ali ibn Mohammed ibn Othman Al Hariri of Basra (God cool his resting-place):

O God, we praise you for what perspicuity you have taught, and what enunciation you have inspired, as we praise you for what bounty you have enlarged, what mercy you have diffused, and we take refuge with you from the vehemence of fluency and the immoderation of talkativeness and the shame of hesitation. And by you we seek to be kept from the temptation of the flattering praiser, and the connivance of the favourer, as we seek to be kept from betrayal of the informer. And we ask pardon if your desire carry us into the region of ambiguities, as we ask pardon if our steps advance to the domain of errors. And we ask that we should be succoured, and given a heart turning with justice, and a tongue adorned with truth, and speech strengthened with demonstration, and accuracy that shall keep us from mistakes, and resolution that shall conquer caprice, and perception by which we may estimate duly, and that you will help us by guidance to conceive, and enable us by assistance to express. That you will guard us from error in narration, and turn us from unseemliness in jesting, that we should be secure from all slander of the tongue, that we be free of the ill of tin-selled speech; that we do not walk in the road of sin, nor stand in the place of repentence, that we are not pursued by suit or censure, nor need to flee from hastiness to excuse. O God, fulfil to us this wish, give us to attain to this desire; do not put us forth of your large shadow, make us not a morsel for the devourer. For now we stretch forth the hand of entreaty to you, we are thorough in humiliation to you and also abasement. And we call down the abundant grace and bounty that is over all, with the humbleness of seeking and with the venture of hope. O God, send down blessing on him and his house who guides aright, and his companions who built up the faith. And make us followers of his guidance and theirs, and profit us all by the loving of him and them, for you are Almighty, and one meet to answer prayer.

THE FIRST ASSEMBLY

THE ENCOUNTER AT SAN'A

I, Harith, son of Hamman, being penniless and in some anxiety of mind, was cast by the hand of Providence to San'a in the Yemen. My wallet was empty, my mind perplexed about my state. Passing through a great concourse of people strolling through the markets, I came upon a thin, frail, black-robed preacher, exhorting the crowd to repent.

"This is somewhat of a diversion," I thought, joining the spell-bound listeners. "I will stop awhile and attend to the rantings of this remarkable fellow, perhaps I may learn something to my advantage here." The people were as close to him as the halo round the moon, or the shell about the oyster.

I got as near as I could to the tall, emaciated-looking preacher, and was immediately attracted by the sound of his voice, the faultless delivery of his words, and the amazing logic of the phrases which fell from his lips almost without a second's pause. His fluency was truly remarkable. Fascinated, the mob, growing in numbers, pressed closer, and I had never heard such flawless rhetoric before, so I strained my ears.

"How long will you all persist in your folly?" he asked, "In your pride and wanton behaviour, against the Knower of your secret, hiding from your neighbour but in the Sight of The Watcher? You conceal evil from your slave but nothing is hidden from your Ruler. You think that your wealth will help you when your judgement day arrives?

How is it that you have not walked in the highway of

guidance, and hastened the treatment of your disease, and blunted the edge of your iniquity, and restrained *yourself* – your chief enemy?

Is not your grey hair your warning? And the grave your sleeping place?

Often has not Time warned you, but have you not preferred slumber? Admonition has pulled you, but you have strained yourself against it. Warnings have been given to you, but you have made yourself blind to these. Truth has been established to you, but you have disputed it; death has made you remember, but you choose to forget.

It has been in your power to impart good but you have not imparted it. You prefer money which you can hoard to piety which you can keep in mind.

You prefer to build a great castle for yourself rather than the bounty which you could offer to others. You turn from the guide who could give you guidance to the pelf which you could gain as a gift. You prefer love of coveted raiment to the recompense which you might earn. The rubies of gifts cling to your heart more than the seasons of prayer. The heightening of dowries is preferred to the continuance of almsgiving.

The dishes of many meats are more desired by you than the leavings of doctrines; the jests of comrades more to you than the reading of the good book.

You command the righteousness but violate its sanctuary; you forbid deceit, but practice it yourself; you fear mankind, but God is more worthy that you should fear Him."

Then he recited:
"Woe to him
that seeks the world,
And turns it
To his careering;
And recovers not from his greediness
For it,
And the excess of his love.

O, if he were wise,
But a drop of what he seeks
Would content him."

Then the preacher fell silent, and made as if to leave. When the company saw that he was going, each man put his hand into a pocket, and gave the good speaker something, each saying: "Use this for your spending, or divide it among your friends."

With half-closed eyes, the preacher thanked them, and turned away, discouraging those who wanted to accompany him further. But I, Al Harith, son of Hamman, followed him secretly, so eager was I to know where he might be staying, and at last (without knowing I was dogging his footsteps) the man disappeared into a cave.

I gave him time to put off his sandals, and wash his feet, before I penetrated into the cave, and an amazing sight met my eyes.

There sat the holy man, being waited upon by an attendant, eating white bread of the finest quality and roast kid, and between them was a jar of date wine.

I felt somewhat cheated, and cried out reproachfully: "O, sir, after what you told us, is this your reality: this luxury, this enjoyment, even wine?"

The peacher stared at me as if he would leap upon me, and appeared almost to be about to burst with rage. Then, his temper cooling, he said:

"I wear the black robe of the preacher to seek my meal, yes, so do I fix my hook in the hardest prey.

"Out of my preaching I make a noose, for Fortune has forced me to make my way even to the thicket of the lion by the subtlety of my beguiling. Yet, do not think that I fear its change, I am steeled against it. Nor does a covetous mind lead me to water at any well that will soil my honour."

While I stood there still speechless, he continued: "Come, and eat, or, if you will, go and tell." Then I turned to the attendant and asked: "Tell me, by Him whose harm is deprecated, who is this?"

And the man answered: "This is Abu Zayd, of Seruj, the Light of Foreigners! The Crown of the Learned!"

Then I turned, and returned from whence I had come, and wondered at what I had seen and heard.

THE SECOND ASSEMBLY

THE ENCOUNTER AT HOLWAN

Wandering hither and thither in search of knowledge, I at last landed at Holwan and found once more the most erudite person in that whole region was none other than Abu Zayd of Seruj. He seemed to change with every wind, sifting among the degrees of pedigree, claiming at one time to be of the race of Sâsân, and at another time he made himself kin to the princes of Ghassân; now he sallied forth in the vesture of poets, and anon he put on the pride of nobles.

Yet, with all this diversifying of his condition, and this display of contradiction, he was adorned with grace and information, and courtesy and knowledge, astonishing eloquence, (which was what had so attracted me to him at San'a) and a foot that mounts the hill of the sciences.

Though he has many faults, one has a fondness for the sight of him, and through the blandishment of his fair-speaking men are loath to oppose him; and through the sweetness of his address he is helped to his desire. Therefore, I kept near him because of his peculiar accomplishments, and valued highly his affection by reason of his precious qualities.

With him I wiped away my cares, and beheld my fortune displayed to me, open of face, gleaming with light. I looked upon his nearness to me as kinship, his remaining with me as wealth, his life as life-giving as rain. Thus we remained a long season; each day he produced some pleasantness for me, and drove some doubt from my heart, until the hand of want mixed for him the cup of parting. The lack of food urged him to abandon Iraq, and he departed, leaving me sad and lonely.

After he was gone none pleased me as he had, and none filled me with a like affection. So he was hidden for a time from me; where he had gone, where he was hiding, I did not know. There was no information I could find of his movements. I went away myself upon a journey for a short while, and when I returned to the place where I had last seen him, which was the library, the council-hall of local scholars, the meeting-place of both residents and visiting strangers, I sat down with the rest.

As we were talking quietly among ourselves, there entered one with a thick grey beard and a most squalid appearance, who saluted us, and took his seat at the rear of the company. He turned to the man next to him, who was reading a book and asked "What is that you are studying?" and the man answered "The poems of Abu Obadeh, he of whose excellence men bear witness." "Indeed," said the squalid one, "And what do you think the best he has written?" "That which I am now reading," said the other, "This line –

'As though she smiled from strung pearls, or hailstones, or camomile flowers.'

For it is a wonder in the use of similes."

"What lack of taste!" cried the man with the thick beard, and everyone turned to look at him and listen to his words, "You have taken for good fat what is only swollen, you have blown on that fuel which is not likely to burst into flame. Where are you in comparison with the rare verse which unites the similarities of the teeth?

'My life a ransom for those teeth whose beauty charms,
And which a purity adorns, rarer than all others.
She parts her lips from fresh pearls, and from hailstones, and from camomile flowers.'. . ."

Then each one approved the couplet, and asked him

to repeat it, and several of them wrote it down, to his dictation and asked "But who has written this, and is he still alive?" And then the reciter smiled and said "My friends, it is the work of him who talks with you today."

One or two looked suspiciously at him, then as if he read their thoughts, the old man with the thick beard quoted from the Koran: "Some suspicions are in sin. O you reciters of verse, truly the purity of the gem is shown by the testing, and the hand of truth tears the cloak of doubt. Let me be tested, let someone challenge me to repeat this type of couplet. So come, I will expose my saddle-bag's contents for comparison."

One man was quick to say "Well, then, compose one after this style, for it is unique, and there is no one who can do the same."

'She rained pearls from the daffodil, and watered the rose, and bit upon the *'unnab (the Chinese Japonica)* with hailstones.'

Before the eyelids had blinked the reply came from the stranger

"I asked her when she met me to put off her rose-red veil,

And to endow my hearing with the sweetest of tidings.

And she removed the crimson light which covered the brightness of her moon,

And she dropped pearls from a perfumed ring."

Then all present were astonished at his wit and readiness, and hastened to honour him, giving him many donations and fine clothes in abundance.

At last I saw that the changed poet was none other than my old friend Shaykh Abu Zayd of Seruj. I hastened to kiss his hand, and said to him "What has changed your appearance and given you a grey beard so that I could not recognize you?"

He smiled and recited the following lines:

"The stroke of calamities makes us hoary, and

fortune to men is a changer.

If it yields to anyone today, tomorrow it overcomes him.

Trust not the gleam of its lightning, for it is a gleam of deceit, and often hides the thunderbolt instead of rain.

But be patient if it hounds calamities against you, and drives them on,

For there is no disgrace to the pure gold when it is turned about in the fire."

Then he rose and departed from that place, and carried our hearts with him.

THE THIRD ASSEMBLY

THE ENCOUNTER AT KAYLAH

I was sitting in a circle of scholars, when one came to us wearing a torn garment, limping painfully towards us, saying:

"O you best of treasures, joy of our kin, health to you all this morning!

Look upon one who was wealthy, master of land and villages, dishes and feasting.

But the frown of calamity came, till the court was empty, the fountain dried, the stables silent, the rooms stone-strewn. I was shod with soreness, my belly was filled with pain, a pit was my home and I deemed thorns a smooth bed.

I thought destroying Death to be sweet and the last day tardy in coming.

And now is there anyone here generous enough to heal, bounteous enough to bestow — for by Him that made me spring from Kaylah, I am now a brother of penury, without a night's feeding?"

I pitied him and pulled out a gold coin for him and said: "If you praise it in verse, then this is yours." So on the spot the lame beggar began:

"How noble is that yellow one, whose yellowness is pure,

Which traverses the regions, whose journeying is afar.

Told abroad are its name and repute; its lines are set as the secret sign of wealth;

Its march is coupled with the success of endeavours;

Its bright look is loved by mankind

As though its ore had been molten of their hearts.
By its aid whoever has gotten it in his purse assails boldly,
Though kindred be perished, or tardy to help.
O, charming are its purity and brightness;
How many a ruler is there whose rule has been perfected by it!
How many a sumptuous one is there whose grief, but for it, would be endless.
How many a host of cares has one charge of it put to flight.
How many a full moon (one in his power and glory) has a sum of it brought down.
How many a one burning with rage, whose coal is flaming,
Has it been secretly whispered to, and then his anger has softened.
How many a prisoner, whom his kin had yielded,
Has it delivered, so that his gladness has been unmingled.
Now by the Truth of the Lord whose creation brought it forth,
Were it not for His fear, I should say that its power was supreme!"

Then he stretched forth his hand after his recitation and said "The honourable man performs what he promises, and the rain-cloud pours if it has thundered."

So I threw him the gold coin and said "Take it, no grudging goes with it."

He put it in his mouth and said "God bless it." He made as if to depart, but there rose in me a strange desire to hear more from him, and I brought out another coin. "Would it suit you too to blame this in the same way, then?" I asked, and he recited with speed:

"Ruin on it for deceit and insincerity,
The yellow one with two faces (the coin) like a hypocrite!

It shows forth with two qualities to the eye of him
that looks at it,
The adornment of the loved one, the colour of the
lover.
Affection for it, think they who judge truly,
Tempts men to commit that which shall anger their
Maker.
But for it no thief's right hand were cut off;
Nor would tyranny be displayed by the impious;
Nor would the niggard shrink from hospitality to the
night-farer;
Nor would the delayed claimant mourn the delay of
him that witholds;
Nor would men call to God from the envious who
casts at them.
Moreover, the worst quality that it possesses
Is that it helps thee not in straits
Save from fleeing from thee like a runaway slave.
Well done he who casts it away from a hill-top,
And who, when it whispers to him with the whisper-
ing of a lover,
Says to it in the words of the truth-speaking, the
veracious,
"I HAVE NO MIND FOR INTIMACY WITH
YOU – BEGONE!"

Then I said to him "How abundant is your flow of
words!" He answered "Agreement binds strongest." So
I tossed him the second gold coin, and said to him
"Consecrate them both with the Twice-Read
Chapter!" and he put it into his mouth with its twin.
Blessing the assembly and its morning's work and the
bounty he had received, the poet turned away to go.
Now I realized by his eloquence that this must indeed
be Abu Zayd, so I called to him and said quietly "You
are recognized, so straighten your walk!" He replied
instantly "If you be Harith the son of Hamman, you
are greeted with honour and may you live long among
the honourable." "I am indeed Harith," I said, "But

what is your condition amid all your fortunes?"

He said "I change between two conditions, distress and ease. I veer with two winds, the tempest and the breeze." I said "And why have you pretended lameness? Surely your kind does not play the clown."

As he moved away he said "I have feigned to be lame, not from love of lameness,

But that I may knock at the gate of relief;

My reins are thrown on my neck, and I go as one who ranges freely.

Now if men blame me I say 'Excuse me, there is no guilt on the lame.' "

THE FOURTH ASSEMBLY

THE ENCOUNTER AT DAMIETTA

I journeyed to Damietta in a year of coming and going, and at a time when I was glanced after for my affluence, desired in friendship, with a group of friends who were all of the same soul as myself. Each of us had a saddled, fleet she-camel, and whenever we had to stop for a short while, or drink at a spring, we snatched the halt and did not waste a moment.

Now it happened that we had been urging on our white camels all night, so that when morning came we were ready to camp. We chose a place where there were dew-moistened hillocks, and a faint east breeze. The groans and moans of the camels continued for a while, then the animals were still at last, as we sat with our feet under us, and the whole caravan came completely to rest.

Sitting quietly, I heard a loud-voiced man say to another "How do you behave to your neighbours and other people?" and heard the reply: "I am friendly to my neighbour even though he might wrong me, and give my fellowship even to the most violent; I bear with a partner though he might be disorderly with my affairs; love my friend even though he drench me with a tepid draught; and prefer my well-wisher even more than my brother; I think little of much if it be for my guest, and overwhelm my companion with kindness. I honour my conversationalist in place of my prince, and hold my intimate to be my peer. I commit my gifts to my acquaintance, confer my comforts on my associate, and soften my speech to him that hates me. I continue to ask after him that disregards me, and am pleased with the crumbs of that which is my due, content with but the last portion of my reward. I do not complain of wrong even when I am wronged, and do not even think of revenge even if a viper stings me."

Then the other said to him "Alas, my boy, only he who clings should be clung to, only he who is valuable should be prized. As for me, I give only to him who will repay, I distinguish not the insolent by my regard, nor will I be affectionate to one who refuses me fair-dealing. I would not aid one who would baulk my hopes, nor be courteous to one who underestimates my value; nor lay aside my menace to the hostile, nor plant my benefits on the land of my enemies, nor show my regard to him who will delight at my death. Nor favour with my gifts any but my friends, nor call to the curing of my sickness any but those that love me, nor make my purpose sincere to him that wishes my decease. I will not pray for him who will not fill my wallet, nor pour out my praise on him that empties my jar.

"For who has judged that I should be lavish and that you should hoard, that I should be soft and you rough, I should melt and you should freeze, that I should blaze and you smoulder? No, by Allah, let us balance each other in speech as in coin, and match in deeds as in sandals; that each to each we may be safe from fraud and free from hatred — for else, why should I give you a full cup of water and you stint me? Why should I bear with you and you condemn me? Why should I gain for you and you wound me? Why should I advance to you and you repel me? For how should fair-dealing be attracted by injury? How can the sun rise clear with cloud? And when did love follow docilely after wrong?

"And what man of honour consents to a state of abasement? For has not your father said this: 'Whoso attaches the affection to me, I repay him as one who builds on his foundation.' And I do to a friend as he does to me, according to the fullness of his meeting or its defect; I make him not a loser, for the worst of men is he whose today falls short of his yesterday.

"Whoever seeks fruit of me gets only the fruit of his now planting.

I seek not to defraud, but I will not come off with the bargain of one who is weak in his reason.

I hold not truth binding on me towards a man who holds it not binding on himself.

There may be one insincere in love who fancies that I am true in my friendship for him, while he is false,

And knows not in his ignorance that I pay my creditor his debt after its kind.

Sunder, with the sundering of hate, from one that would make you a fool, and hold him as one entombed in his grave.

And towards him in whose intercourse there is aught doubtful put on the garb of one who shrinks from his intimacy.

And hope not for affection from any who sees that you are in want of his money."

Now, when I had heard all this from these two, I longed to know them in person. When dawn came, and the sun was rising, I went out before the camels had risen from their knees, and began to search for that night-voice which had so excited me.

At last, looking upon all the faces of the travellers, I came upon Abu Zayd and his son talking together, wearing thin, worn cloaks. I knew them to be the ones I sought, and I made myself known, offering them a removal to my lodgings, pitying their shabbiness, and treated them as one enamoured of their refinement. I told the others of their worth, and shook fruit from many branches for them.

At last they were taken for valued friends by many, and received gifts; almost overwhelmed, in fact, with largess.

Now we were in a night-camp, and from there we

could see the villages beyond, and spy the fires of hospitality burning there. Abu Zayd, seeing that his purse was full, and his distress alleviated, said to me "Truly I am a disgracefully dirty creature at this time. Permit me to go quickly to that village and go to find water, that I might shine in this company."

I said, "Yes, do that if you wish, but go, and quickly return."

"I shall," said he, "appear again quicker than the glancing of your eye," and he called to his son "Come, hurry, hurry"; then they were both gone.

So we stayed and watched for them as men watch for the new moon, and later sent scouts and spies to the village. But they found no trace of Abu Zayd there. Then I said to my companions: "We have wasted time enough here, and waited over-long for him; let us go now, and speedily, he will not return." Each man began to prepare for departure, and then I found a letter pinned to my saddle-bag: "O thou who wast to me an arm and a helper, above all mankind! Reckon not that I have left thee through impatience or ingratitude; for since I was born I have been of those who 'when they have eaten, separate.' " Then I made the company read the words of the Book so that he who might have blamed Abu Zayd might excuse him. And they admired his witticism, but commended themselves from his further mischief.

THE FIFTH ASSEMBLY

THE ENCOUNTER AT KUFA

Once, conversing at Kufa, when the moon was an amulet of silver in the sky, I had the good fortune to meet with much good talk and learned discussion. Each of those there was a man to remember from, not guard against; each was one his friend would incline to, not avoid. And the night talk fascinated us until the moon had set, and it was time to sleep.

Then, suddenly, there was the sound of knocking on the outer gate, and the barking of watch-dogs.

We said "Who is it at this time of night?" and the reply was:

"O people of the mansion, be you guarded from ill!
Meet not with harm as long as you live!
The night has driven one to your abode,
A brother of journeying, dust-laden,
Who has been lengthened, extended
Till he has become bent and yellow
Like the new moon of the horizon when it smiles . . .
And now he approaches your courtyard, begging boldly
And repairs to you before all people else,
To seek from you food and a lodging.
You have in him a guest contented, ingenuous,
One pleased with all, whether sweet or bitter,
One who will withdraw from you publishing your bounty."

Now, when we were caught by the sweetness of his pleas, we hastened to open the gate, and brought him up and met him with welcome. And we said to the cook's boy: "Quick, bring to eat whatever is ready."

Then said our guest "By Him that has sent me to you, I will not roll my tongue over your food unless you pledge me that you will not make me a burden. For sometimes a morsel aches the eater and forbids him his repast. And the worst of guests is he who imposes trouble and annoys his host. And especially with a harm that affects the body and tends to sickness; for as the proverb has it 'The best suppers are those that are clearly seen' . . . Which only means that supper-time should be hastened and that eating by night, that dims the sight, should be avoided. Unless, by Allah, the fire of hunger kindle and stand in the way of sleep."

When the boy brought what there was to be had, we lighted a large candle, and I saw that it was none other than Abu Zayd. So I said to the company "Joy to you of the guest who has come! For if the moon of Sirius has gone down, truly the moon of poetry has arisen."

Then the glow of happiness came to them all, and thought of sleep faded. They refused the rest they had been debating, and spread pleasantries before Abu Zayd. "Please tell us one of your stories," I urged eagerly, "Or one of the wonders from your journeys."

"The wonders I have met with no seers have seen, no tellers have told," he said. "But among the most wondrous was that which I beheld tonight, a little before coming to your gate." Then we bade him tell.

"Truly the hurlings of Fate have thrown me to this land at a strange time. I was in hunger and distress, and when the dark had settled I rose, in spite of all my footsoreness, to seek a host, or to gain a loaf. Then the driver Hunger, and Fate, (the Father of Wonders) urged me on, till I stood at the door of a house, and spoke, improvising:
"Hail people of this dwelling,
May you live in the ease of a plenteous life!
What have you for a son of the road, one crushed to

the sand,
Worn with journeyings, stumbling in the night-dark
night?
Aching in entrails, which enclose naught but
hunger?
For two days he has not tasted the savour of a meal;
In your land therefore there is no refuge for him.
Already the van of the drooping darkness has
gloomed,
And through bewilderment he is restless.
Now in this abode, is there anyone, sweet of spring,
Who will say to me 'Throw away your staff and
enter,
Rejoice in a cheerful welcome and a ready meal?' "
"Then there came forward a lad in a tunic who said to
me 'By the sanctity of the Shaykh who ordained
hospitality, we have nothing in our hall for the
wayfarer but conversation and a lodging.'

"I said 'What shall I do with an empty house, and a
host the ally of penury? But tell me, good youth, what
is your name?'

" 'My name is Zayd,' he answered, 'and my birthplace Fayd; and I came to this place yesterday with
my mother's people, the Benu 'Abs. My mother Burrah
told me (and she is like her name, 'pious') that she
married in the year of the foray on Mawan a man of
the nobles of Seruj and Ghassan. But when he was
aware of her pregnancy (he was a crafty bird, it is said)
he made off from her by stealth, and he has stayed
away.

'Nor is it known whether he is alive, to be looked for,
or if he is in his cold tomb.' "

Said Abu Zayd "Now I know by sure signs that this
was my own child, but the emptiness of my hand
turned me from making myself known to him. So I
parted from him with heart crushed and tears unshed.

"And now, you men of wonder, have you ever heard
anything more remarkable than this?"

We said "No, by Him who has knowledge of the Book."

He said "Write it, for it is a wondrous tale," and we sent for the ink-flask, and its snake-like reeds, and we wrote the story elegantly as he worded it. After which we wanted to draw him out more on the subject of the boy, and said "Do you wish to have the child?" and he answered "If my purse were heavy then to take charge of my son would be light."

"If an appropriate sum of money would help you, we could collect it at once," we said.

"And how could an appropriate sum of money not content me? Any man who refused would indeed be a madman!" he said. Then each of us took a share in it, and wrote an order for him, whereupon he gave us thanks, and praised us greatly.

The whole night passed in his telling us such delightful tales that they shamed the wonderful stuffs of Yemen. The dawn appeared, and light-bearing morning went forth.

As soon as the sun came, Abu Zayd said "Let us go and get this money, for my heart yearns for my child."

So I went with him, to make easy his success.

As soon as the money was in his hand, his face shone with joy. "May you be rewarded!" he cried, "May God be my substitute towards you!"

I said "I would like to go with you to see this noble son of yours, if I could follow you."

Then Abu Zayd looked at me and laughed till the water ran from his eyes, saying:

"You have thought the mirage to be water when I told you what I did! By Allah, I have no Burrah as a wife, no son named after me! Nothing is mine except various kinds of magic in which I am original, and copy no one. I have to use these to reach whatever my hand would pluck.

"If I were to abandon them, my state would be changed, and I would not gain what I do now.

"I ask you to excuse me, and pardon me if I have done any wrong."

Then he took leave of me and left coals of fire in my breast.

THE SIXTH ASSEMBLY

THE ENCOUNTER AT MERAGHAH, OR 'THE DIVERSIFIED'

I happened to be present in the Court of Supervision at Meraghah when the talk ran of eloquence. All those present agreed who were the knights of the pen, and lords of genius; that there remained no one who could select his diction, or use himself freely in it as he willed; and that, since the men of old were gone, there was none now left who could originate a brilliant method, or open a virgin style. They said that even one marvellous among the writers of this age, and holding in his grasp the cords of eloquence, is but a dependent on the ancients.

Now, there was sitting on the outskirts of this assembly an elderly man, in the place reserved for the attendants, and his nostrils quivered almost in pain as several things were said with which he clearly did not agree.

It was obvious that he was a twanger of the bow who shapes his arrows, who sits in wait desiring the conflict. When the quivers of invention were empty, he turned to the company and said "You have uttered a grievous thing; you have wandered much from the way. For you have magnified mouldering bones, you have been excessive in leaning towards those who are gone; you have condemned your generation, among whom you were born, and with whom your friendships were established. Have you forgotten, you skilful in testing, you sages of loosing and binding, how much new springs have given forth, how the colt has surpassed the full-grown steed? Have you forgotten with your refined expressions, and delightful metaphors, and ornate addresses, and admired cadences? And if anyone here will look diligently, is there in the work of the ancients anything but the ideas whose paths are worn, whose ranges are restricted? Which have been handed down from them through the priority of their birth, but not from any superiority in him who draws first at the well over him that comes after? Now truly I know one who when he composes, colours richly, and when he expresses, embellishes; and when he is lengthy, finds golden thoughts, and when he is brief, baffles his imitator, and when he improvises, astonishes, and when he creates, cuts the envious."

Then the President of the Court said to him "Who is it that strikes on this rock, that is the hero of these qualities?"

And he said "It is the adversary of this your skirmish, the partner of your disputation. Now, if you will rein a good steed, call forth one who will answer, so you shall see a wonder."

Said the President (the Eye of those Eyes), "Stranger, the rook in our country is not taken for an eagle, and with us it is easy to discern between silver and shingle. He is rare who exposes himself to the conflict and then escapes mortal hurt; or who stirs up the dust of trial and then escapes the mote of contempt. So do not offer your honour to shame, do not turn from the counsel of the counsellor."

He answered "Each man knows best the mark of his own arrow, and be sure the night shall disclose its own morn."

Then the company whispered as to how this well might best be fathomed; and his proving undertaken, and one said "Leave him to me, that I may pelt him with the stone of my story, for it is the tightest of knots, the touch-stone of testing." Then, the others invested him with the command of the business, and he said "I am attached to the Governor and maintain my condition by ornamental eloquence.

"Now, in my country I could rely for the straightening of my crookedness by the sufficiency of my means, coupled with the smallness of my family. But when my back was weighed, and my thin rain failed, I repaired to him from my home with hope, and besought him to restore my comeliness and competence. He looked pleasantly on my coming, and was gracious, and served me morning and evening.

"But when I sought permission from him to return to my house, on the shoulder of cheerfulness, he said 'I have determined that I will not provide you with supplies, I will bring no scattered means together for you, unless before your departure you compose an address, setting down the true facts of your state, in such a way that the letter of one of every two words shall have all dots, while the letters of the other shall not be pointed at all.' And now I have waited for my eloquence for a twelve month, but it has not returned. I have roused my wit for a year, but only my sluggishness has increased. I have asked help from all the scribes, but each of them has frowned and drawn back. Now if you have disclosed your character with accuracy, come with a sign if you be truthful."

Then the elder answered "You have put a good steed to the pace; you have sought water at a full stream; you have given the bow to him who fashioned it; you have lodged in the house him who built it." Then he thought a while, till he had let his flow of wit collect, and said:

"Take your ink flask, take your implements and write:

"Generosity (May God establish the host of your successes) adorns; but meanness (may fortune cast down the eyelid of your enviers) dishonours; the noble rewards, but the base disappoints; the princely entertains, but the niggardly frightens away; the liberal nourishes, but the churl pains; giving revives but deferring torments; blessing protects, and praise purifies; the honourable repays, for repudiation abases; the rejection of him who should be respected is error; a denial to the sons of hope is outrage; and none is miserly but the fool, and none is foolish but the miser; and none hoards but the wretched, for the pious clenches not his palms. But your promise ceases not to fulfil; your sentiments cease not to relieve; nor your clemency to indulge; nor your new moon to illuminate; nor your bounty to enrich, nor your enemies to praise you; nor your blade to destroy; nor your praiser to win; nor your kindness to succour; nor your heaven to rain, nor your milk-flow to abound; nor your princeship to build up; nor your suitor to gain; nor your refusal to be rare. Now, he who hopes in you is an old man like a shadow, one to whom nothing remains. He seeks you with persuasion whose eagerness leaps onwards. He praises you with choice phrases, which merit their dowries. His demand is a light one, his claims are clear, his praise is striven for, his blame is shunned. And behind him is a household, whom misery has touched, whom wrong has stripped, whom squalor involves. And he is ever in tears that come at call, and trouble that melts him, and care that is as a guest, and growing sadness. On account of hope that has disappointed him, and loss that has made him hoary, and the enemy that has fixed his tooth in him, and the quiet that is gone. And yet, his love has not swerved, that there should be anger at him, nor is his wood rotten, that he should be lopped away, nor has his breast spit foulness that he should be shaken off; nor has his intercourse been forward that he should be hated. Now your honour admits not the rejection of his claim, so whiten his hope by the lightening of his distress: then will he publish your praise throughout the world. So may you live to avert misfortune, and to bestow wealth; to heal grief and to care for the aged; attended by affluence and fresh joyousness; as long as the hall of the rich is visited, or the delusion of the selfish is feared. And so Peace."

Now when he had ceased from the dictation of the address, and showed his prowess in the strife of eloquence, the company gratified him by word and deed, and made him many compliments and gifts.

Then he was asked what tribe was his origin, and what valley was his home, he answered:

"Ghassan is my noble kindred, and Seruj my ancient land.

There my home was like the sun in splendour and mighty rank.

And my dwelling was as Paradise in sweetness, pleasantness and worth.

O, excellent was the life I led there and plenteous the delights.

In the day that I drew my broidered robe in its meadow, sharp of purpose,

I walked proudly in the mantle of youth, and looked upon goodly pleasures,

Fearing not the visitations of time and its evil haps.

Now if grief could kill, surely I would die from my abiding griefs;

Or if past life could be redeemed my good life's blood would redeem it.

For death is better for a man than to live the life of a beast.

When the ring of subjection leads him to mighty trouble and outrage,

And he sees lions whom the paws of assailing hyenas seize,

But the fault is in the time: but for its ill-luck character would not miss its place;

If the time were upright, then would the conditions of men be upright in it."

After this his story reached the ears of the Governor, who filled his mouth with jewels and bade him join his followers, and preside over his Court of Public Writing.

But the gifts sufficed him, and the unwillingness restrained him from public office. I had recognised the wood of his tree before the ripening of his fruit. But he had hinted to me by a twinkle of his eye that I should not bare his sword from its sheath. And when he was going away, full of purse, and victorious, I escorted him to the door, chiding him for refusing office, and giving him all courtesy as I bade him farewell.

He turned away with a smile, saying:

"To traverse the lands in poverty is dearer to me than rank,

For in rulers there is caprice and fault-finding; O, what fault-finding!

There is none of them who completes his good work, or who builds up where has laid foundation.

So let not the glare of the mirage beguile you; undertake not that which is doubtful;

For how many a dreamer has his dream made joyful, but fear has come upon him when he awoke."

THE SEVENTH ASSEMBLY

THE ENCOUNTER AT BARKAID

I had determined on journeying from Barkaid, but on noticing the signs of the coming feast, decided to stay until I had witnessed the day of adornment. So when it came with its usual rites, under constriction or of free will, I do not know which, I followed the tradition in new apparel, and went forth with the people to keep the festival.

Now, when the congregation of the prayer court was gathered together, and ranged, and the crowding stifled men's breath, there appeared an old man in two thin cloaks, his eyes fast closed, and upon his arm what looked like an old horse-bag. There was guiding him an old woman, small and wizened like a goblin.

Then he stopped, like one who is tottering, wishing to sink down in fatigue, and when he was greeted spoke in a feeble voice. When he had replied, he put his fingers into his wallet, and brought out scraps of paper that had been written on with coloured inks. He gave them to the old dame, and bid her hand out each one. Now, it was my fate to have allotted to me a scrap on which was written:

"I have become crushed with pains and fears;
Tried by the proud one, the crafty, the assailer,
By the traitor among my brethren, who hates me for my need,
By torment from those who work to undo my toils.
How oft do I burn through spites and penury and wandering;
How oft do I tramp in shabby garb, thought of by

none.

O, would that fortune when it wronged me had slain
my babes!

For were not my cubs torments to me and ills,

I would not have addressed my hopes to kin or lord,

Nor would I draw my skirts along the track of
abasement.

For my garret would be more seemly for me, and
my rags more honourable.

Now is there an honourable man who would see that
the lightening of my loads must be by a dinar;

Or will quench the heat of my anxiety by a shirt and
trousers."

When I had looked upon these verses, I longed for
knowledge of him that had fashioned them. I realised
that my way to him would be through the old woman,
and knew that a fee to the ancient informer was
necessary.

So I watched her, as she was wending her way
through the rows of people, row by row, begging a dole
of the hands, hand by hand, but no purse shed
anything on her palm.

So, where her soliciting was baffled, she went to each
person, and took back the scraps of paper. But
somehow she did not come to me for the return of my
piece. She went to the old man, and wept that she had
been thus denied. All he said was "In God's hands I
am, to God I commit my case; there is no strength or
power but by God." Then he recited:

"There remains not any pure, not any sincere; not a
spring, not a helper;

But of baseness there is one level; not any is trusty,
not any is of worth."

Then he said to her: "Cheer your soul and collect
the papers, and count them." She answered "I have
collected them, and counted them when I asked them
back, and I found that one of them had seized the
paper."

He said "Perdition on you, wretch; go and find it." As soon as she came towards me, I got the paper ready to give her, and put a dirhem and a mite with the paper, and said: "If you have a fondness for the polished, and the engraved," and I pointed to the larger coin, "show me the secret, the obscure. But, if you will not explain, then take this mite instead of the dirhem, and begone."

So she said, wishing to get the coin of larger value, "Ask what you will."

Whereupon, I asked her of the old man, and what was his country, and of the poem, and who wrote it.

"Truly," she answered, "the old man is of the people of Seruj, and he it was who wrote that poem." And she snatched the dirhem with the snatch of a hawk, and shot away like an arrow. But it troubled my heart that perchance it was Abu Zayd who was indicated, and my grief was great that, if it were he, he should be blind, and in such straits. I wanted to go to him, and talk to him, and question him, but I could not do so without treading on the necks of the rest of the congregation, a thing forbidden by the law. So I sat in my place, till the sermon was at an end, and I managed to go quickly to him. I examined the old man, and his closed eyes, and I saw it was indeed Abu Zayd.

So I made myself known, and presented him with one of my tunics, and invited him to share food with me.

So we set forth, my hand leading him, my shadow his conductor. Now, when we had seated ourselves in my own room, he asked me "Is there anyone here with us?" I replied "There is no one here but the old woman, and ourselves." He said "I have no secrets from her," and opened his eyes.

I was overjoyed that he was not blind, after all, but wondered at his strangeness at pretending thus.

"Tell me" I asked, "what made you feign blindness, you, with your journeying in desolate places, your traversing of wildernesses, and your discovering of distant lands?"

But he pointed to show that his mouth was full, and he indicated that he could not with politeness speak at that time, and kept well busied with his meal. Then, when his needs were satisfied, he turned his full gaze upon me and recited:

"Since Time (and he is the father of mankind) makes himself blind to the right in his purposes and aims,

I, too, have assumed blindness, so as to be called a brother of time — what wonder that one should match oneself with one's father!"

Then he said to me, "Please go to the closet, and bring me alkali that it may clear the eye, and clean the hand, and soften the skin, and perfume the breath, and brace the gums, and strengthen the stomach. And let it be fragrant of odour, new of pounding, delicate of powdering, so that one smelling it would imagine it to be camphor. And join with it a toothpick choice in material, delightful in use, and let it have the slimness of a lover, the polish of a sword, the sharpness of a lance of war, and the pliancy of a green bough." So I rose to get him what he wished for, thinking that I would please him, and went to the closet. But when I returned, in less time than it takes to tell, I found that the room was empty, and that the old man and the old woman had fled. I was angry at his disappearance, and looked everywhere for him, but he was as one who had sunk to the bottom of the sea, or had been borne aloft to the clouds.

THE EIGHTH ASSEMBLY

THE ENCOUNTER AT MA'ARRAH

At one time I was attending the court presided over by the Kadi of Ma'arrah, and two men came before the Kadi, one was old and the other young.

Said the old man "God strengthen the judge, as by him He strengthens whoever seeks judgement. I had a slave girl, elegant of shape, smooth of cheek, patient to labour. At one time she ambled like a good steed, at others she slept quietly in her bed. Even in July you would find her touch to be cool. She had understanding and discretion, sharpness and wit, a hand with fingers, yet a mouth without teeth. She was now hiding, now peeping forth, fitted for employment, obedient in poverty and in wealth, if you spurned her, she showed affection, but if you put her from you, she would remain quietly apart. Generally she would serve, but sometimes she would pain you, and trouble you.

"Now, this young man asked me to lend her to him for a service of his own, and I made her his servant, without reward. The conditions were that he would enjoy the use of her, but that he would not burden her with more than she could bear. But, he forced on her too hard work, and extracted of her long labour, and then he returned her to me, broken in health, offering compensation which I will not accept."

Now it was the young man's turn to speak, and he said "The old man is truthful in all that he says, but as for my hurting her, it was all a mistake. I have pledged to him in equal payment of the damage, a slave of mine, of equal birth, free from stain or disgrace, whose

place was the apple of his master's eye. He showed
kindness, he called up admiration, if he was placed in
power he was generous, if he marked anything for
himself he was noble with it; if he was supplied, he
would give of his supply, and when he was asked for
more, he added. He did not stay in the house, and rarely
visited his wives, he was generous with his possessions,
he was lofty with his bounty."

"Now," said the Kadi to them both "either explain,
or depart, for I cannot understand you."

The the young man came forward and explained:
"The old man lent me a needle with which to mend my
rags, which much use has blackened. When its eye
broke by accident in my hand, as I drew the thread
through it, the old man was furious with me saying
'Give me a needle like it, or a price, after you have
mended it!' And he keeps my Kohl pencil by him as a
pledge, and my eyes are dry through my not having it."

The Kadi turned to the old man and asked:
"Will you speak now, and explain further?"

"I swear by the holy place and the devout whom the
slope of Mina brings together, if Time had been my
helper, you would not have seen me taking in pledge
the pencil which he has pledged to me. Nor would I
bring myself to seek a substitute for the needle that he
has spoiled, no, nor the price of it. To know my condition is to know his; misery, and distress, exile and
sickness. Fortune has put us on a level – I am his like
in misery, and he is as I. He cannot ransom his pencil
now that it lies in my hand, and through the
narrowness of my own means, it is not within my
bounds to forgive his offending."

Now when the Kadi had heard their stories, and
learned of their penury and of their distinction, he took
out from under his cushion a dinar and said "With this
you should end and decide your contention."

The old man caught it before the youth, and claimed
the whole of it in earnest, saying to the young man

"Half of this is mine as my share of the bounty, and your share is mine, in payment for the needle! But I will be just, so come and take your pencil."

The young man became downcast, at the words of the old man, and the Kadi, too, became sullen, as he thought about the lost dinar. The Kadi tried to cheer the young man by doling out a few dirhems to him, saying "Put away these wranglings, and avoid disputes, and do not come before me with these arguments, for I have no purse of fine-money for you!" Then the Kadi turned to his attendants, and said "I have a strange idea that these two are not suitors as they claim to be, but practisers of craft, do you not agree? But, what is the way to fathom their art, and draw them out?"

Then the most knowing one of his assembly said "Surely the discovery of what they hide must be through themselves." So the Kadi had the two claimants brought back, and when they stood before him he said:

"Tell me truly your camel's age, so shall you be secure from the consequence of your deceit."

Then the younger shrank back and asked for pardon, but the old man stepped forward boldly and said "I am the Seruji, and this is my son, the cub at the proving is like the lion. Neither his hand nor mine has had anything to do with either needle or pencil, only fortune, the hostile, has brought us to this. We came forth here to beg of each one whose palm is moist, whose spring is sweet. By every art, with every aim, by earnest, if it prospered, and if not, by jest. We hoped to draw forward a drop for our thirsty lot, and consume our life in wretched victual. Death is on the watch for us, if he falls not on us today he will fall on us tomorrow."

Then the Kadi congratulated him on his words, his honesty, and yet told him "Take care when you come before judges again, for in every season you might not be excused, or your speech listened to."

So the old man departed, with the guile still on his brow, promising to follow this wise counsel.

THE NINTH ASSEMBLY

THE ENCOUNTER AT ALEXANDRIA

The liveliness of youth and the desire for gain sped me on until I had gone all the way from Ferghana and Ghanah. I had listened to the words of the wise, and plunged into perils to reach my needs; I had learned that when one enters a strange city the best thing to do is to go to the Kadi and seek his favour.

So I took trouble to find where the Kadi was situated when I entered the city of Alexandria. I felt it might be safer in a new place, in case I got into any sort of litigation.

Now, when I was in the company of the judge of Alexandria one cold evening, and he had brought out the alms-money to distribute among the needy, there entered his presence an ill-looking old man whom a young matron was dragging along.

She said "God strengthen the Kadi and through him make concord everlasting! I am a woman of excellent stock, whose root is most pure, and my mother's and father's kin are of the most honourable. My character is moderate, my disposition contentment, and my nature is to be a good helpmate. My father looked for a good and wealthy husband for me among the wooers which were offered, and this man came and said that he strung pearls, and made a great deal of money from this trade. My father believed him, and willingly gave me in marriage to him. But when he had taken me away from my own people, and removed me to his home, I found him to be lazy, a lie-a-bed, a slumberer! I had come with all fine clothes to him, with good furniture, and jewellery. But it was not long before he had sold all my belongings in the market-place, until everything was gone that was mine. So I said to him, 'Rise up now and earn with your trade the money that we need. I am not being difficult to please, I hope, I know that there is no music after the wedding, but I do think that you should make some attempt to support me.'

"But he declared that his trade had been struck with slackness owing to the violence that was abroad in the world. I was distressed, because he had left the house as cleared of valuables, as naked as the palm of my hand. Also, I have a boy by him, thin as a tooth-pick, and neither of us gets any food from him, we are hungry all the time. So I bring him before you, Kadi, that I should have some justice, and you should test him and find out if what I have said is true or not."

Then the Kadi turned to the man and said "You have heard your wife's testimony; now testify yourself, and explain the why and the wherefore of this matter. If you are guilty you must surely go to prison."

The man looked down for a few moments, then he replied: "Hear my story, there is laughter in it, and there are tears. I am a man in whose qualities there is no blame, neither is there any suspicion on my glory. I am from Seruj, and my stock is Ghassan, and study is my business, to dive deep into learning is my pursuit, and what a wonderful search it is indeed! My capital is the magic of speech, out of which I mould both verse and prose. I dive into the deep of eloquence, and from it I choose the pearls and select them. I take phrases of silver, and when I have moulded them men say they have turned to gold. Now, formerly I got great wealth from my calling, and many were the presents brought to me from the rich and powerful. My foot rose to high ranges where there were no further steps. But today learning is a chattel of slackest sale in the market of him on whom hope depends; the honour of its sons is not respected, neither are relationships and alliance with them regarded. It is as though they were corpses in their courtyards, from whose stench men turn aside and withdraw. Now my heart is confused by my trial with the times, so strange is their changing. The strength of my arm is straitened by the straitness of my hand's means, grief and care assail me. And my fortune, the blameworthy, has led me to the paths of that which honour holds as base, for I sold my belongings until there remained not a mat in my room. So I indebted myself until I had a heavy debt, and I starved myself for five days, trying to think of a way. But when my entrails were wrapped in hunger, when hunger scorched me, I could see nothing but her goods, and though I knew it wrong, I had to do it. I dared not ask her for permission, because I knew that that would not be granted, so I went ahead secretly selling so that we could eat even a little.

"If what angers her is that she fancied that it was my fingers that did the stringing, I am sorry; I swear by Him to whose Ka'beh the companies journey when the fleet camels bear them onwards, deceit towards chaste ladies is not my nature; since I was reared nothing has attached to my hand but the swift-moving reeds and books; for it is my wit that strings necklaces of pearls, not my hands. It is this craft I meant when I said that I was a stringer of pearls. So give ear to my explaining as you have listened to her, and show respect to neither, but judge as you should."

Now, when he had completed his tale and became silent, the Kadi turned to the young woman, and said "It is settled among all judges and all those who bear authority, that generous times have gone, and the present times incline toward meanness. Now, I imagine that your husband is truthful in all that he has said, and free from blame. For he has acknowledged his debt to you, and has explained everything. He has proved by these words that he can string them perfectly, and that he is bare to the bone in poverty. Now to censure him who shows true excuse is base, to imprison the destitute is a sin, to conceal poverty is self-denial, to await relief with patience is devotion. So return to your home and pardon the master of your virginity. Refrain from using your tongue sharply and submit to the will of your Lord." Then in alms-giving he gave them a golden coin, and said: "Refresh yourselves with this, and endure against the trouble of the times, for God will bring victory."

Then, thanking the Kadi, they rose to go, and the man was like one who exulted in affluence after need.

I knew that he was Abu Zayd when I had heard his first few words, and the woman reviled him. But I was very distressed later on to hear that someone had seen him laughing and clapping his hands with a friend, and reciting some humorous lines which ended something like this:

"I was near falling into trouble through an impudent jade,

And should have gone to prison but for the Kadi of Alexandria!",

Unfortunately, too, the Kadi himself heard this, and sent one out to find him, and explain what the joke was, but Abu Zayd was nowhere to be found.

The Kadi then began laughing, and said to me, "I should not have harmed him (God forbid that I should imprison men of letters!), but I would have liked to say to him that *'The latter state would have been better for him than the former.'* "

THE TENTH ASSEMBLY

THE ENCOUNTER AT RABAH

The summoning of desire beckoned me to Rabah, the city of Malik, son of Towk, and I obeyed it, mounted on a fleet camel.

When I had got myself lodging there, and gone out after a bath and a shave, I saw an old man pulling by the arm a most handsome youth, and shouting "Death to him! Vengeance! He has killed my son!"

So many people gathered round the couple, and such was the hubbub, that at last they were carried off to the court of the Governor of the city. When they were there, the old man renewed his charge, and demanded help in the matter from the law.

So the Governor made the boy speak, for he had become fascinated by the remarkable good looks of the young fellow. And the boy said: "It is a lie! I am no blood-shedder. It is the slander of a knave against one who is no assassin."

The Governor said to the poor, weeping old man "If two Moslems testify for you, then all will be well. If not, demand the oath of him."

"He struck my son down in a place remote from men, and shed his blood when they were alone," said the old man, angrily, "How can I have a witness in such a situation? But empower me to dicate the oath so that it will appear to you whether he speaks truth or lies when he swears it."

Said the Governor, "You have authority for that, you with your vehement grief for your slain son." And then the old man said to the boy: "Say, I swear by Him that has made forelocks on foreheads, eyes with black and white, and eyebrows with separation, and smiling teeth with regularity, and eyelids with languor, and noses with straightness, and cheeks with flame, and mouths with purity, and fingers with softness, and waists with slenderness, that I have not killed your son by negligence, nor of wilfulness, nor made his head a sheath for my sword. If it be otherwise, may God strike my eyelid with soreness, and my cheek with freckles, and my forelocks with drooping, and my palm-shoot with greenness, my rose with the ox-eye, my full moon with waning, and my silver with tarnishing, my rays with the dark."

Then said the boy: "The scorching of affliction would be more easy to take than this oath! Let me yield to vengeance rather than take an oath such as this, swearing as no one has ever sworn before!"

But the old man insisted that this oath was the only one which he should swear. The dispute between them continued to rage. The Governor, deciding that he wanted to save this young man from the old one, wanted to rescue him, and enslave him himself. So he said to the old man "Have you not a mind for that which is more seemly and God-fearing?"

"What do you mean?" cried the demented father.

"I mean," responded the Governor, "that you should in the light of reason cease from this altercation and accept a hundred dinars in settlement of the case."

"On condition that I take some of it now," said the old man. So the Governor paid him twenty, and collected some more from his attendants, making up the sum of fifty dinars.

But night came on, and it was getting dark, and the collection of dinars was thus cut short, so the Governor said "Take this amount, and leave disputing; tomorrow I will have the rest made up to you."

Said the old man, "I will do this on condition that I can keep the youth with me tonight, and bring him back to you tomorrow. The pupil of my eye will guard him."

Now I was there while all this was going on, and I knew the old man to be, of course, Abu Zayd of Seruj, so I challenged him, as he was guarding the boy, and made myself known.

"Yes," he admitted; and when I said "Who is this boy?", he said "He is my own."

I asked him "Are you going to let the Governor get hold of him, then?" He smiled, and said "Pass the rest of the night with me, that I may enjoy your company during this remaining time; but listen, I have resolved to slip away at dawn, and thus burn the Governor's heart with the flame of regret."

Then I spent the night with him in conversation more pleasant than a garden of flowers, or a woodland of trees. And when the Wolf's Tail lightened the horizon, he left with the boy. But before he departed he handed me a letter, firmly sealed, and said "Give this to the Governor when we are safely gone."

But I could not resist breaking the seal, and read his writing:

"Tell the Governor whom I have left biting his fingers, that the old man has stolen his money and the young one his heart, and he is scorched with the flame of a double regret. He was generous with his coin when love blinded his eye, and he has ended with losing both.

"You have got in exchange understanding and caution, and the wise man, the prudent, wishes for these.

"So hereafter resist desires, and know that the chasing of gazelles is not easy; every one who seeks to take a prey sometimes becomes a prey himself.

"But consider well, and do not forecast every thundercloud; many a thundercloud may have in it the bolts of death. Cast down your eyes, that you may rest from a passion by which you could cloth yourself in a garment of infamy and disgrace. For the trouble of man is the following of the soul's desire; and the seed of desire is the longing look of the eye."

I tore the paper to shreds, and cared not whether he blamed or pardoned me.

THE ELEVENTH ASSEMBLY

THE ENCOUNTER AT SAWEH

I was aware of hardness of heart when I sojourned at Saweh, so I decided to go to the public burial ground there, for the purpose of contemplation, as our tradition requires. I was meditating on those of my own who were gone. When I reached there, I saw that there were some people standing over a newly covered grave. There was an old man, cloaked, and leaning on a stick, who mounted a hillock, and addressed us, with veiled face: "Let those who work, work for an end like this," he cried. "Now, take thought, you who are lazy, and you who are negligent, look well, and observe what I am saying.

"How is it that the burying of your fellows does not grieve you, that the pouring in of the mould does not frighten you, that you do not heed the visitations of misfortune; that you do not prepare for going to your graves, that you are not moved to tears by the eye that weeps, that you do not take the warning of the death-message when it is heard; that you are not frightened when an intimate is lost, that you are not saddened by the gathering of the mourning ones? One of you follows the dead man's bier home, but his heart is set on getting his house; he is present at the burying of his kinsman, but his heart is set on securing his portion. He leaves his beloved friend with the worms, then retires alone with his pipes and his lutes.

"You have sorrowed over your riches if but a grain were notched away, but you have been forgetful of the cutting off of your friends. You have been cast down at

derstanding time antithetical to Hallaj

ed

the befalling of adversity, but have made little of the perishing of your own kind. You have laughed at a funeral as you have not laughed in the hour of dancing. You have walked wantonly behind funerals, as you did not walk in the day that you grasped gifts. You have turned from the recital of mourning women to the preparing of banquets and from the anguish of the bereaved to daintiness in feasting. You care not for him that moulders, and you do not move the thought of death in your mind. So that it is as if you were joined to Death by clientship, or had got security from Time, or were confident of your own safety, or had made some sort of a pact with the Destroyer of delights. No, it is an ill thing that you imagine, again no! Surely you shall learn.

"O you who claim understanding, how long, O brother of delusion, will you marshal sin and blame, and err exceeding error? Is not the shame plain to you? Does not hoariness warn you (and in its counsel there is no doubtfulness), nor has your hearing become deaf. Is not Death calling you? Does he not make you hear his voice? How long will you be bewildered, and walk proudly in vanity, and go eagerly to diversion, as if Death were not for all?

"How long will your serving last, and your delay to mend habits that unite in you every vice? If you anger your Master you are not dismayed, but if you find something goes wrong with one of your schemes, you are bursting with frustration at it.

"If the yellow one gleams to you, you are joyful, but if the funeral passes you, you pretend grief, but there is no real grief.

"You resist him who counsels you rightly, you are hard in understanding; you swerve aside, but you follow him who deceives, defames, lies.

"You walk in the desire of your soul, you scheme after money, but you forget the darkness of the grave, and do not remember what there is there.

"But if true happiness had looked on you you would not have been led astray by your own look; and you will weep blood, not tears, when you find that no company can protect you in the Court of Assembling.

"It is as though I could see you when you go down to the vault below; when your kinsmen have consigned you to a place narrower than the needle's eye. There is the body stretched out that the worms may devour it. And afterwards there is no escape from the reviewer of souls, since Sirat is prepared, its bridge is stretched out over the fire to everyone who comes. How many a guide shall go astray, and how many a great one shall be vile, and how many a learned one shall slip and say 'The business surpasses'. Therefore hurry, simple one, to that which by the bitter is made sweet, and know that your life is now near to decay and you have not withdrawn yourself from blame. Do not rely on fortune, though it be soft, though it be gay, for so you will be found like one deceived by a viper that spits venom.

"Lower yourself from your loftiness, for death is meeting you and reaching at your collar; and he is one who does not shrink back when he has decided to come.

"Avoid turning away if the cheek of fortune has prospered you; bridle your speech if it would run away, for how happy is he who bridles it!

"Believe the brother of sorrow, and believe him when he speaks; and mend your ragged conduct, for he who does benefits; and plume him whose plumage has fallen out in calamity, and sorrow not in loss, and do not be covetous in amassing. Resist your base nature, and accustom your hand to liberality, and listen not to blame for it, and keep your hand from hoarding.

"Make provision for the good of your soul and leave that which will bring on ill, and prepare the ship for your journey, and feel fear for the depth of the sea.

"Thus have I given my precepts, friends, and shown

as one who shows clearly, and happy is the man who walks by my doctrines and makes them his example."

Then he drew back his sleeve, and the people went to him, and filled his sleeve. Then, he came down from the hillock, smiling happily. I pulled him by the cloak, and it was Abu Zayd, in all his deceit. I said to him "How many, Abu Zayd, are the varieties of your cunning to drive the prey to your net? And will you not care who censures?"

He answered without shame and without hesitation: "Look well, and leave your blaming; for tell me, have you ever known a time when a man would not win from the world when the game was in his hands?"

"Away with you, Old Shaykh of Hell, laden with infamy!" I cried, "There is nothing like you for the seeming fairness of your speech and the foulness of your purpose, except silvered dung or a whitened sewer." Then we parted; I went to the right and he went away to the left, I to the south, and he to the north.

THE TWELFTH ASSEMBLY

THE ENCOUNTER AT DAMASCUS

Being well provided with money, the master of many horses, and envied wealth, I made the journey from Iraq to Ghutah. When I reached the place, I found it as tongues had described it, and there was in it all that souls desire, and eyes delight in. I began to break the seals of desires and gather the cluster of delights.

Until some travellers were getting ready for the trip back to Iraq, I did not think of my home and my own people. Then I struck the tents of exile and saddled the steeds of return. And when the company had equipped themselves and all was ready for the start, we began to search for one that would be a guard for us. We sought from every tribe and used a thousand devices to obtain him, but we could not find one.

The travellers were then somewhat bewildered, and assembled at the gates of Jayrun to take counsel. Every suggestion was made, every hope exhausted. Then we saw a person whose demeanour was of youth, his garb was that of a dervish, in his hand was the rosary of women made from aloes. His eye was that of the watchful, he had fixed his gaze on us, and sharpened his ear to what was being discussed.

When there was a quiet moment, he said to them "O people, let your care relieve itself, let your mind be tranquil, for I will guard you with that which shall put off your fear and show itself in accord with you."

Then we asked him to show us concerning his safeguard and promised him a higher wage for it than for an embassy.

Then he declared that it was some protection made from talismanic words that had come to him in a dream, with which to guard himself from the malice of mankind, a shibboleth of power.

So we looked at each other sideways, and it became apparent that no one believed this, and thought his story to be a lie. Whereupon he said "How is it that you do not believe me, and treat my gold as dross? Now, by Allah, often have I gone through the most dreadful dangers, and fearful desert tracts, and with this I need no accompanying guard or quiver of arrows. Besides, I will remove what gives you doubt, I will draw away the distrust that has come upon you, I will go with you and accompany you over the Semaweh, the Syrian desert. Then, if my promise is proved true, you can reward me; if it is proved that I have lied, you may cut my skin and pour out my blood."

Then we were inspired to believe his vision, and we took as true what he had related. We ceased from disputing, and cast lots as to whom he should go with. After the pack saddles were fastened on, and the time for setting forth was near, we each tried to learn from him the magic words that we might make them a lasting safeguard.

He said "Let each of you repeat the Mother of the Koran (the first chapter) as often as night or day comes on, then let him say with lowly tongue and humble voice: 'O God, O You who give life to the mouldering dead, Who avert harm, Who guard from terrors, O You generous in rewarding, O You the refuge of suppliants, You, Lord of pardon and protection, send the blessing on Mohammed, the Seal of your prophets, the Bringer of Your messages, and on the lights of his kindred, the Keys of his victory! And give me refuge, O God, from the mischief of devils and the assaults of princes, from the vexing of the wrongers, and from suffering through tyrants; from the enmity of transgressors, and from the transgression of enemies, and from the conquest of conquerors, from the spoiling of the spoilers, from the crafts of the crafty, from the treacheries of the treacherous. And deliver me, O God, from the wrongfulness of neighbours and the neighbourhood of the wrongful; and keep me from the hands of the harmful, bring me forth from the darkness of the oppressors, place me by Your mercy among Your servants who do right. Keep me in my own land and in my journeying, in my exile and in my coming home, in my foraging and in my return from it, in my trafficking and my success from it, in my adventuring and in my withdrawing from it. And guard myself and my property, in my honour and in my goods, in my family and in my means, in my household and in my dwelling, in my strength and in my fortune, in my riches and in my death. Do not bring reverses upon me, make not the invader lord over me, but give me from Yourself helping power.

"O God, watch over me with Your eye, and Your aid, distinguish me by the safeguard and the bounty You have for us, befriend me with election and good, and consign me not to the keeping of any but You. But grant to me health that does not wear away, and allot to me comfort that does not perish, and free me from the terrors of misfortune, and shelter me with the covering of Your boons. Do not let the talons of my enemies prevail against me, for You are He who hears prayer."

Then he looked down, and was silent. So we said "A fear has come upon him that has either confounded him or struck him dumb." Then he raised his hand and drew his breath and spoke again: "I swear by the heavens with the constellations, the earth with its plains, the pouring flood, the blazing sun, and the sounding sea, and wind and the dust-storm, that this is the most sure of charms, one that will best suffice you for the wearers of the helmet. He who repeats it at the smiling of the dawn has no alarm of dangers to the red of eve, and he who whispers it to the vanguard of the night is safe the whole night long from plunder."

So we learned it till we knew it thoroughly, and rehearsed it together that we might not forget it. Then we set out, urging the beasts by prayers, not by the songs of drivers; and guarding the loads by words, not warriors. Our companion frequented us evening and morning, but did not require of us any of our promises. Then when we spied the housetops of Anah, he said to us: "Now, your help, your help!"

Then we set before him our merchandise, the exposed and the hidden, and opened for him the corded and the sealed. We said to him: "Decide and choose as you will, for you will find that we are all in agreement that you should be greatly rewarded."

Nothing delighted him but the coin, the light, the adorning. So he took all he required to repair his poverty, and then he slipped away from us as quick as mercury does. We were sad to see him go, and his suddenness of departure was strange to us, after the time we had been together.

We asked news of him from all and sundry, till one said "Since he entered Anah he has not ceased from drinking in the tavern."

So I went by night to the wine-hall in disguise, and there was the old man in a gaily-coloured dress among casks and wine-vats. There were around him cup-bearers of surpassing beauty, and lights that glittered, and the sweet scents of myrtle and jasmin, and pipe and lute. At one time he bid me broach the wine-casks, and at another be begged the lutes to give utterance, and now he inhaled the perfumes, and now he courted the gazelles. But I said to him "Woe to you, accursed! Have you forgotten the day at the Jayrun?"

But he laughed heartily, and then most charmingly quoted to me these words:

"I cling to journeying, I cross deserts, I loathe pride

that I may cull joy:
And I plunge into floods, and tame steeds that I may
draw the trains of pleasure and delight,
And I throw away staidness, and sell my land, for
the sipping of wine, for the quaffing of cups.
And were it not for the longing after the drinking of
wine, my mouth would not utter its elegancies,
Nor would my craft have lured the travellers to the
land of Iraq, through my carrying of rosaries.
Now, be not angry, nor cry aloud, nor chide, for my
excuse is plain:
And wonder not at an old man who settles himself in
a well-filled house by a cask that is brimming,
For truly wine strengthens the bones and heals
sickness and drives away grief,
And the purest joy is when the grave man throws off
the veils of shame and flings them aside;
And the sweetest of passion is when the love-crazed
ceases from the concealing of his love, and shows it
openly.
Then avow your love and cool your heart, or else the
fire-staff of your grief will rub a spark on it,
And heal your wounds, and draw out your cares by
the daughter of the vine, she the desired;
And assign to your evening draught a cup-bearer
who will stir the torment of desire when she gazes;
And a singer who will raise such a voice that the
mountains of iron shall thrill at it when she chants;
And rebel against the adviser who will not permit
you to approach a beauty when she consents,
And range in your cunning even to perverseness;
and care little what is said of you, and catch what
suits you;
And leave your father if he refuse you, and spread
your nets and hunt who comes by you,
But be sincere with your friend, and avoid the
niggardly, and bestow kindness, and be constant in
gifts;

And take refuge in repentance before your departure for whoso knocks at the door of the Merciful causes it to open."

Then I said to him "Congratulations on your most rare recitation, but shame on your misconduct! Now, by Allah, tell me from what thicket is your root, for the puzzle that you are confuses me."

He said "I do not like to disclose myself, but I am the novelty of the time, the wonder of nations, I am the wily one, one who plays his wiles among Arabs and foreigners; but none the less a brother of need, whom fortune vexes and wrongs; and the father of children who lie out like meatballs on the tray. Now the brother of want, who has a household, is not blamed if he be wily."

Then I knew that it was Abu Zayd, the man of ill-fame and disgrace, he that blackens the face of his hoariness. The greatness of his roguery offended me, and I thought of the foulness of his path. So I said to him indignantly and with the confidence of acquaintance: "Is it not time, old man, that you withdrew from debauchery?"

But he was angry, and growled, and his face changed, and he thought for a while. Then he said "It is a night for merriment, not for rebuke, an occasion for drinking wine, not for contention: so leave speaking your thoughts until we meet tomorrow."

I left him, through fear of his drunken condition, with no confidence in his promise, and I passed the night mourning. I made a vow to Allah that I would never again enter the tavern of the liquor-seller, even though I were endowed with the dominion of Baghdad, and that I would not look upon the vats of wine, even if my youth were to be restored to me.

Then I and my companions saddled the white camels in the last darkness of the night, and left behind those two old ones, Abu Zayd and Iblis, the Devil, and rode away.

THE THIRTEENTH ASSEMBLY

THE ENCOUNTER AT BAGHDAD

I was in company with some Shayks of the poets, on the banks of the Zowra, the Tigris, in the neighbourhood of Baghdad, and they were such that no rival could even keep up with their dust.

We flowed in a discourse together till we had halved the day. Now, when we were finding our thoughts failing, and we were thinking of rest, we caught sight of an old woman, who approached from the distance. She was leading some children, as thin as spindles, and as weak as doves. When she saw us, she began to make towards us, and standing before us, said "Know, O you who are the refuge of the hoping, the stay of the widowed, that I am of the Princes of the tribes, the ladies who are kept jealously. My people and my husband were wont to settle on the Breast, and to journey at the Heart, to burden the Back, to advance the Hand; but when Fortune destroyed the Arms, and pained the Liver by means of the Limbs, and turned about till Back was Belly, and the Eyeball grew dim, and the Eyebrow restless, and the Eye went forth, and the Palm was lost, and Forearm grew dry, and the Right Hand broke, and the Elbows departed, and there remained to us neither Front Tooth nor Eye Tooth. Since the Green Life has become Dust-Coloured, my White Day has been made Black, and even the Greek, the Blue-eyed enemy, has pitied me, and now I welcome the Red Death!"

Knowing that she spoke in the poetic sense, I understood that what she was saying was that her people and her husband were wont to sit in the first place in the assembly, to march at the centre or at the head of the army; they conferred favours; but when Fortune destroyed those who helped them, and afflicted them by taking away their children and their servants, who laboured for them and brought them gain; and when their state was overthrown, then whoever looked on them with respect withdrew, their attendants were insolent, the coin was withdrawn, their quiet was lost, so was their power, and even the Greeks, the Blue-eyed enemy, pitied her, and she now wanted death in battle (the Red Death); and so we stopped to question her. I said "I am amazed at your beauty of metaphor, your prose has certainly enchanted us! How is your poetry?"

"Without a boast," said she, "it would make a rock gush forth water." She uncovered her crafty old face, and standing there in her well-worn smock, recited to us:

"I complain to God, with the complaining of the sick
Against the trouble of the unjust, the hateful time.
O, friends, I am of people who prospered long ago, while the eyelid of fortune was cast down before them;
Their glory then was remarkable,
And their fame was spread abroad among men!
When foraging failed in the ashy year (the year of drought) they were a goodly meadow;
Their fires were kindled to the travellers, and they fed the guest with fresh meat;
Their neighbour passed not his night in hunger, not through fear did he say 'Choking hinders me'.
But the changes of destruction have made their seas of bounty to sink away from them, which I thought would not ever sink;
And put away from among them, into the bowels of the earth, those that were lions of guarding, healers of the sick.

That on which I carry is now my back, after being
my beast, and my home is in the hollow, after being
on the height.
My little ones fail not to mourn their misery, of
which there is some each day,
When the pious man prays to his Lord by night,
they also call to Him with gushing tears.
O You who feed the young raven in the nest, and set
the bone which is broken, and again broken;
Appoint to us, O God, one whose honour is pure
and washed from the filth of blame;
Who will quench for us the fire of hunger, though
only with a mess of sour milk,
For, by Him to whom the forelocks shall bow down
in the Day when the faces of the assemblage shall be
black and white (the Believers white with joy and
infidels black with despair).
Were it not for these, my cheek would not expose
itself, nor would I assay to the stringing of verse."

How she cleft our hearts with her verses, and called
forward the gifts of our wallets. And when her sleeve
was filled full with gold, and each of us had shown
bounty to her, she retreated, the little ones following
after her, and her mouth was wide with her thanks.

But after she was gone, the company was all agog to
know where she might have gone, and they wondered
how to fathom her history.

So I decided to go in search of the old woman, to
find out for them, and to see where the little family
were living, and to find out if we might help them more.

I found her tracks, and finally came into a street
choked with people, thronging in several directions.
There she drew away from the simple children and,
leaving them behind, went into the shadow of a ruined
mosque.

Through a chink in the door I spied her throw aside
the veil, toss the woman's cloak into a corner, and
reveal the face and figure of Abu Zayd.

Meaning to rush in upon him and rebuke him, I made as if to upbraid him. But at that moment he began to sing a strange song, the words of which I will always remember:

"O, would that I knew whether the time had got knowledge of my power,
Whether or not it had learnt the real truth of how deep I go in deceiving;
How many of its sons have I won by my wile and my fraud!
How often I have sallied forth in my known form and disguise,
To catch one set by preaching; another by poetry;
To excite one mind by vinegar, and another by wine.
Now if I had followed the frequented path all the length of my life,
My fire and my portion would have failed, my need and my loss would have lasted.
So say to him who blames: 'Here is my excuse — take it'."

When this was ended, and the clearness of his case came to me, I knew that Abu Zayd's devil was a rebellious one, who would not listen to rebuke, and would do nothing but what he willed. So I turned back without speaking to him, and left him to the counting of his gold. I told my companions when they questioned me about what I had seen, and they became sullen at the loss of their money, and vowed to one another that they would in future deny all old women, but I pondered long and deeply upon what I had heard him sing.

THE FOURTEENTH ASSEMBLY

THE ENCOUNTER AT MECCA

I went to Mecca Makarama, to perform pilgrimage, and having fulfilled the usual rites, and permitting myself perfume and indulgence, I was sitting under a leather tent with a polite company.

The noon blinded the eye of the chameleon, and through all that excessive heat there tottered an old man, followed by a good-looking youth. The old man hailed us with the greeting of the well-bred, the intelligent, and answered us with the answering of a kinsman, not a stranger. We asked him "What are you, and from where do you come, that you have no reserve before us?"

And he answered: "I am a suppliant, a seeker of help; the secret of my misery is not hidden, and one look at me is my sufficient intercessor. As for my intrusion, to which suspicion would appear to cling, why, it is not unexplainable, surely seeing there can be no veil over the generous."

Then we asked him how he had found his way to us, and he replied at once "True generosity has a fragrance whose breathing steals forth, whose odours guide to its meadow: I was led to you this way."

Then we asked him what was his need, and what the boy with him needed, and how we could help him.

"I have a need," he said, "and my boy has a request."

We said "Tell us, and both wishes shall be granted."

"By Him who has spread out the seven worlds," he said, "I thank you." And then he spoke these lines:

"I am a man whose beast has fallen with soreness of foot and weariness;

My distance is a far one, my pace is unequal to it.

With me there is not so much as a mustard seed of the stamped gold;

My contriving is closed up, my bewilderment plays with me.

If I set out on foot, I fear destructive haps:

And if I lag behind the company the way is straitened;

My sighing is on the heights, my tears are on the slopes;

But you are the foraging grounds of him that hopes, the target of seeking;

Your grist pours down as the clouds do not;

Your neighbourhood is in sanctuary, but your wealth is open to spoiling;

The terror-stricken does not take shelter with you, and then fear the tooth of calamity;

Nor does he that hopes seek the milk-flow of your gifts, and then fail to be gifted.

So now be moved by my story, and prosper from my retiring from you,

For if you had made trial of my life, of its meat and its drink,

Surely such distress as mine would pain you, distress that gives me up to sorrows.

And if you were to learn my distinction, and my pedigree, and my path

And what my knowledge embraces of choice studies,

No doubt it would occur to you that my breeding is my malady.

Now, would that I had not sucked at the breast of scholarship,

For its ill-luck has fallen on me; and in this thing was my father dutiless to me."

We said to him: "Your verses have now disclosed to

us the fact that you are poor, that your she-camel has died. So we will mount you on another that will take you on; and now, what is the wish of your son?"

He said "Rise, boy, as your father rose and spoke, rise and speak what is in your mind!"

The boy rose heroically and recited:

"O lords, whose dwellings are built upon high places,

Who, when danger befalls, take stand to ward off stratagem;

To whom is easy the bestowing of stored-up treasure,

I desire a loaf, bread, a piece of roast meat, and a pudding;

But if that is too dear, then let it be crackling in which there be hidden some shreds of roast lamb;

But if this be denied, then mere dates with their juice.

Please bring what is easy for you, even if it be but shreddings of dry meat;

And pray make it quickly, for my soul is longing for what is ready.

For there is no doing without provision for my far journey;

And you are the best of kindred to be called upon in an emergency and necessity;

Your hands every day are full of new bounties,

Your palms bestow all sorts of useful gifts.

Now my wish will limit itself within the folds of that which you shall give.

Through me many rewards may be got; and estimable is the consequence of relieving my sorrow;

And mine are young offsprings of the wit which puts to shame every poem."

Now, when we saw that the cub was like the lion, we mounted the father and fed the son. They spread out their thanks to us like robes of honour, and paid us that way.

When they were all ready for departure, I said to the

old man "Has our promise been fulfilled to your liking?" and he answered "Your kindness has been mighty and manifest."

So he and the boy left us, and I knew that they had been given all that they needed, and more than that Abu Zayd would not extract from the City of Mecca, so aware was he of her great beauty and tranquillity.

THE FIFTEENTH ASSEMBLY

THE ENCOUNTER CALLED 'THE LEGAL'

I was passing a sleepless night, and desiring someone to help me pass it, was delighted to hear a knock upon my door.

"Perhaps the plant of wishing has borne fruit," I thought, and hastened to open. "Who is it?" I called with my hand upon the latch.

"A stranger," was the reply, "whom the night has caught in darkness, whom the rain-flood has caught. When it dawns, I will continue my journey."

So I opened the door, smiling, for I knew that voice, and realized that night-talking with him would be wonderful. "Enter with peace," I said happily, and Abu Zayd stepped into the room.

I put food before him but he withdrew from it. I looked at him in amazement, for this was a change in him. "Why are you upset like this? Tell me your condition," said I.

"I was at sunrise yesterday in a great market place," he said, "where I saw rows and rows of cornelian dates, that had been summered in a favourable place; and opposite them was fine fresh milk, that showed a creamy gleam, flavoured with saffron. Then appetite bound me with its cord, and thirst brought me under its dominion. I remained more distracted than a lover, more bewildered than a lizard, for I had no means with which to satisfy my hunger and thirst. I walked about, trying to find some way to earn some money, but work of any sort or charity of any kind eluded me, until at night I had a burning feeling in my stomach. Then I met a Shaykh, who was lamenting with the lamentation of the bereaved, weeping copiously.

"I felt no more my own pain and asked him: 'O stranger, tell me the secret of your sorrow, for you will find in me a physician to cure or a helper to impart.'

" 'By Allah!' he cried, 'my lamenting is not after livelihood that is gone, nor fortune that is insolent, but for the perishing of science, and the going down of its suns and moons.'

" 'And what has made you so grieved in this instance?' I queried.

"Then he drew forth a scrap of paper and said that he had taken it everywhere to have it deciphered, and no one could read it aright. 'Let me have it,' I said, 'and I will try to make out what is written there.' I took it up and read:

"O, the learned, the lawyer, who surpasses in judgement, and acuteness, there is none like you!

Give me a decision on a case that every judge shuns, at which every lawyer is bewildered.

A man died, leaving a brother, both by father and mother, who was a Moslem, free, pious;

And the deceased had a wife who had, O Doctor, a brother, really her own, without equivocation;

She got her legal share, and her brother took what was left of her inheritance

Instead of the deceased's brother.

Now relieve us by your answer as to what we ask."

"When I had read the verses on the paper and seen what they meant, I said to him 'You have fallen on one who knows it, you must give me a meal and I will tell you what it means.'

"He said 'You are just in your stipulating, and have shrunk from excess; come to my home and I will feed you generously.'

Said Abu Zayd: "Then I followed him to his house, which was narrower than the ark of Moses, weaker than a spider's web, but he gave me the choicest

victuals, and all that I desired to eat. After I had filled
myself with the delicious dates and creamy milk that
ended the meal, he said 'Now, come, here is my ink-
flask and pens, dictate an answer to that which you
have just read me.'

"I dictated the following:

"Say to him who sets riddles that I surely am the
discloser of the secret which he hides.

Know that the deceased, in whose case the law preferred the brother of his spouse to the son of his
father,

Was a man who, of his own free consent, gave his
son in marriage to his own mother-in-law; nothing
strange in that.

Then the son died, but she was already pregnant by
him, and gave birth to a son like him;

And he was the son's son without dispute, and
brother of the grandfather's spouse without
equivocation.

But the son of the true-born son is nearer to the
grandfather, and takes precedence in the inheritance
over the brother;

And therefore, when he died, the eighth of the
inheritance was ajudged to the wife for her to take
possession;

And the grandson, who was really her brother by
her mother, took the rest.

And the full brother was left out of the inheritance
and we say you have only to bewail him.

That is my decision which every judge who judges
will pattern by."

"Now when he had understood the answer," continued Abu Zayd, "and verified its correctness, he said
to me 'Remember the family and the night, so gather
up your skirts and be beforehand with the rain-flood.' I
said 'I am in exile, and in sheltering me lies the best of
offering. Especially as the darkness is coming, and the
thunder is lauding God in the sky.'

"He said to me 'Be off (and may God keep you too), go wherever you will, but do not ask to spend the night here.'

"I said 'Why not?' and he said: 'Because I did look well and saw how you swallowed what was before you, and you left nothing. Now, he that exceeds in what you have exceeded, and fills his belly as you have filled it, will not escape a weakening surfeit nor a killing cholera. So go from my house while you are still well, for by Him that gives life and death there is no lodging in my house.'

"Now, when I had heard his oath, I went out of his house, with sadness. The sky rained on me, and the darkness made me stumble, and dogs barked at me, and doors repulsed me, until I came to your door by the kindness of fate."

Then I said to Abu Zayd "This ordained meeting is dear to my heart!" and he began to divert me with more stories, and to mix the laughable with the mournful, till the first of the morning dawned, and the caller of "Blessing" made his cry. Whereupon Abu Zayd made ready to respond to the caller, and then turned and bid me farewell.

"Hospitality is three days," I reminded him but he gave me another quotation:

"Visit him whom you love in each month only one day; and exceed not that;

For the beholding of the new moon is but one day in the month,

And afterwards eyes look not upon it. . . ."

Then I took leave of him, and he of me, and my heart was still sorrowing long after he had gone.

THE SIXTEENTH ASSEMBLY

THE ENCOUNTER OF THE WEST

I was performing the prayer of sunset at one of the mosques of the West, and when I had finished it, my eye fell on a company of people who were sitting aside from others, deep in friendly conversational exchange.

I approached them, as they were rubbing the fire-staves of discussion, passing the cup of talk from mouth to mouth. So I advanced upon them and said "Will you receive a stranger to your circle? I desire the beauty of dialogue, the pleasure of night-talking." And they said "Welcome, welcome, join us!" I had no sooner joined them, than there came upon us a dusty wanderer, on whose shoulder there was a scribe's wallet. He greeted us in the mosque, saying "O you men of understanding! Do you not know that the choicest of offerings is the relieving of sorrows, and the firmest cord of salvation is the imparting to those who have need? Now, by Him who has set me down in your midst, and destined to me the asking of alms of you, truly I am the stray of a distant abode, the messenger of empty-bellied children. And is there in this company any that will cool for us the heat of hunger?"

Then they said to him "O Stranger, you have come after the evening meal, and there only remain the leavings, but take them if you can be content with those." He said "The brother of affliction is content with the smallest scraps and even the shakings out of provision bags." Each of them asked his servant to give the stranger what remained, and he was duly grateful for

the food provided in this way. He thanked us, and
joined us in conversation. We began to talk about how
it would be possible to make verses if each of us were
to think of one line. So the man who proposed it began
thus: "Blame him who wearies of you," and the one
next to him spoke this line: "Make great your hope of
the recompense of your Lord." Another said: "He who
completes the kindness which he renders, gains
increase." Then yet another: "Silence every one who
blabs to you, and you will be wise." Then it was my
turn, and I could think of nothing, and I said to my
companions "If Abu Zayd the Seruji were present here,
he would cure this cureless malady of mine." We began
to declare that it was hard to follow the others, and
that the door of imagination was shut. But the stranger
glanced at us with the glance of the contemptuous, and
he called out "O people! truly it is a great thing to
make the barren give birth, and there is One learned
above all the learned." Then he turned to me and said
"I will take your place, and free you from what has
fallen on you. Now, if you desire to speak in prose, and
yet not to trip, say, addressing him who blames
avarice, and is large in his reproach, say 'Take refuge
with every trusty patron who, when he had collected
and possesses, gives freely'; but if you prefer to versify,
say to him whom you esteem:
  'Bestow on the needy when he comes to you, and
  show regard even when a man injures you.
  Have dealings with him that is noble, but put afar
  from you him that is base.
  Withdraw from the side of the unjust, the mis-
  chievous, when he sits by you,
  When contention rouses itself put it off from
  yourself, and cast it away.
  Be still, and you shall grow strong; for it may be that
  the time that was perverse to you shall aid you.'
Now, when he had bewitched us like that with his
fine verses, and fatigued us by the remoteness of his

goals, we praised him till he begged to be spared from our flattery, and we gave more to him until he said it was enough. Then, he gathered up his garment, and rose to go, saying:

"How excellent is this company, who are true of speech, princes in wordy beauty.

They surpass mankind in far-famed virtues, they surpass them in their gifts.

And I alighted among them, begging; and met with rain that poured.

I testify that if the generous are a shower, they are a Flood!"

Then he stopped the distance of two lances from us and said: "The face of the highway is now veiled, for the darkness has come. Have you a lantern that I could borrow and make my way safely home?"

And when that was brought, I saw in the light that the stranger was Abu Zayd, and I told the company "This is he of whom I have spoken to you, the Seruji, who when he speaks, hits the point, and when he is asked for rain he pours." Then he and I were happy when the company asked him to pass the night in talk with us, on condition that they would mend his poverty-stricken condition.

He said "My desire is yours! Welcome to you all, since you have welcomed! Nevertheless, when I came to you my children were writhing with hunger, calling to me for a quick return. If they find me tardy, distress will possess them, and my life will be no more serene. Let me go that I may relieve their state, and fill their emptiness, then I will return to you for night-talking until dawn."

So we said to one of the lads, "Go with him to his people, and bring him quickly back here." And the boy set out with him, carrying Abu Zayd's wallet under his arm, hastening his return.

Then the lad came back alone. "What has happened?" we cried to the young fellow. He said "He took me a long way, with branching paths, till we came to a ruined hut. 'Here it is,' he said, 'the nest of my chicks.' Then he pulled away from me his wallet, saying 'By my life, you have lightened a load for me, and deserve good treatment from me. Listen to this, it is fair counsel:

'When you have got the plucking of the date palm, do not defer it till the coming year.
When you have got to the threshing-floor, fill your crop with the ears that are there;
And do not stay when you have picked them up, in case you stick in the net of the fowler:
And do not go far in when you swim, for safety lies on the bank.
Accost with "Give now" and answer with "Bye-and-bye"; and sell what is promised to you for what comes at once,
And exceed not upon a friend in your visiting, for no one was ever wearied of one except the clinging guest.'

"Then he said 'Treasure these lines, learn them by heart and follow them in your conduct. Now, hasten to your people, and tell them that I send my greeting, and tell them full surely that nights spent in tale-telling are among the greatest of harms!' "

THE SEVENTEENTH ASSEMBLY

THE ENCOUNTER CALLED 'THE REVERSED'

Upon one of my journeys, I was drawn to a group of youths whose understanding was great, and wanted to be with them, judging the fruits of their disputing to be sweet. And when I had joined myself to them, and strung myself on their thread, they asked "Are you one who will pride himself in proving himself in the strife of wordy battle?"

But I said "No, I am one of the lookers on at war, not one of the sons of the stab and the stroke". Then they broke off from arguing with me, and began asking each other riddles. There was in their midst, an old man whom care had made lean, whom the hot wind had scorched, whom the sun had made brown. But, listening to him, I admired the remarkable judgement with which he was gifted, and his surpassing wit in that assembly. When the asking and the answers were exhausted, he hinted that he had one or two more arrows left in the quiver of thought. They said: "Excellent, please let us see them", and he began: "Do you know a composition whose earth is its heaven, and whose morn is its evening; which is woven on two beams, and shows with two colours, and prays towards two points, and goes forth with two faces? If it rises from its east, excellent is its splendour, and if it mounts from its west, then it is marvellous!"

The company was struck with speechlessness, and no man said a word. When he saw them, dumb as cattle, he said to them "If your minds yield freely I will commend you, so rub the spark of your fire-staves."

They said "By Allah, there is no swimming in this sea, no wandering on its shore . . ." He smiled at them, and said: "Take down this in dictation, and hand it down from me.

"Man is the creature of kindness, and the perfecting of a benefit is the deed of the liberal, and the disposition of the generous is a treasure of praise; the practice of courtesy leads of necessity to affection, the bond of friendship demands sincere counsel, the truth of narrative is the ornament of the tongue, the eloquence of speech is witchcraft to hearts, the net of desire is the bane of souls, the impatience of disposition is a dishonour to mortals, and the clinging of prudence is the leading-cord of safety; to seek occasions for blaming is the worst of faults; dwelling upon failings overthrows friendship; sincerity of purpose is the cream of gifts; ungrudgingness in conferring is the price due to asking; and the undertaking of labours lays the way for recompense. Faith in God's protection makes it easy to bestow, and the excellence of the prince is the largeness of his breast; the ornament of rulers is the hatred of defamers; the reward of praiseworthy deeds is the bestowing of gifts; and the dowry of conciliation is the obtaining of requests; the cause of error is extravagance of aim; and to overstep bounds blunts vigour; and transgression of politeness nullifies services; and the forgetting of rights provokes resistance; to shun doubtful deeds raises men's rank; and elevation of dignities is by rushing into dangers; and the exalting of positions is by favour of Providence; and loftiness in actions is through the limiting of desires; and the lengthening of thought makes precision of judgement; and the crown of princeliness is the refinement of courtliness; and by contentiousness is lost what is sought for; and in perils is shown the difference between men. In the superiority of plans lies the distinction of men's values; and by the exaggeration of the envoy policy is weakened; and through laxness of powers do terrors appear; and by the task of patience is the fruit of victory; and the merit to be praiseworthy is in proportion to diligence. To repay regard is necessary to consideration, and affection in servants is shown in visiting their masters; and the adornment of manliness is the guarding of trusts; the proving of brethren is the lightening of one's griefs; and the repulse of enemies is by defence on the part of friends, and the testing of the ignorant is by associating them with the ignorant. The looking to consequences gives security from fatalities; and the keeping from baseness spreads reputation; the vice of boorishness consists not with excellence; and the essence of the noble is the guarding of secrets."

Then he said: "These are two hundred words comprising culture and admonition. If one moves them in this direction, there is no debate, no contention. If one desires the reversing of their mould, and the turning of them backwards, let him say 'Secrets are trusted to the noble, and the nature of excellence consists not with boorishness, and the foulness of reputation spreads disgrace.' And so on this track let him trail them and not fear error in them, until there shall come the close of their couplets and the last of their pearls, namely 'To perfect kindness is a good deed of man'."

Now when he had uttered this unique address, we knew how much composition may be diverse in merit, and that excellence is in the hand of God; He gives it to whom He will. Then we clung to his skirt, and each gave him a portion of what he possessed. But he would not take mine, saying "I do not take forfeit from my pupils." I said "Be Abu Zayd, even with all this embrowning of your figure and this leanness of your cheek!" And he answered "Yes, I am he, even with all my withering." Then I started chiding him for all this gadding east and west. Then he said:

"Time has drawn his blade upon me to fright me, and has sharpened his blade.

He has stolen away from my eyelid its slumber, like
an adversary, and made its tears flow,
And caused me to roam the world; to go to its East,
to traverse its West;
And day after day there is for me in each valley but
a single rising and setting,
And so the exile's figure is changed and his destination is afar."
The aching of my throat followed him as he went,
swinging his arms. We were divided between turning to
gaze at his retreat and hastening after him. Then we
loosed our loops, and we went in all directions, like the
bands of Saba.

THE EIGHTEENTH ASSEMBLY

THE ENCOUNTER AT SINJAR

I was once on the return journey to Damascus, on my way to the City of Peace, with travellers of the Benu Nomayr, a company of wealth and worth. And with us was Abu Zayd of Seruj, he that is an enchainment to the hasty, and a beguiling to the bereaved. Now, our halting at Sinjar fell on a time when one of the merchants there was making a marriage feast, and he asked to the banquet the whole community, both men of settled land and the desert. His invitation embraced the important and those of no account, so his bidding extended to the caravan train as well. Now when we had responded, and arrived at his house, he set before us all that is sweet to the mouth and fine to the eye, and after that he brought out a huge glass vase, which was as though it had been congealed air, or composed of sunbeam motes, or moulded of the light of the plain, or peeled from the white pearl. It had been filled with an assortment of sweets, and it exuded a wonderful scent. Our appetites were rekindled at the sight of it, and we were all eager to sample its delights. But suddenly Abu Zayd sprang up like a madman, and removed himself as far away as the fish is sundered from the lizard. We sought him and would bring him back to the table, but he refused, saying "By Him that raises the dead from their sepulchres, I will not return unless that vase be taken away!" So we had it removed from sight and he resumed his seat. When he was settled once more, we asked him why he had flown, and he said: "Because that glass is a betrayer. For years I have had an oath that the same place should not hold me and one that betrays." We asked "Tell, what is the cause of this strict vow?"

He said "I had a neighbour whose tongue cajoled, while his heart was a scorpion; whose speech was a honeycomb to refresh, but whose hidden thought was a concentrated venom. Through his living near me I was led into converse with him, and by his false smiling I was deluded into consorting with him. The fairness of his seeming infatuated me to accompany him about, and the guile of his character drew me into intimacy with him. I associated with him in the belief that he would be to me as a most close neighbour, then I found out that he was as a swooping eagle. I was familiar with him, thinking that he was a friend, but he showed that he was a treacherous serpent. I ate my salt with him, and knew not that at the end he would be as one whose loss is rejoiced at; I drank my wine with him, and never at that time knew that he would be of those whose departure is a delight.

"Now, in my house there was a maiden to whom no rival could be found in perfection. If she unveiled, the two lights of heaven were shamed, and if she smiled she made beads of silver despised, and pearls would be sold for what is worthless. If she gazed, she roused love-fancies and she realized the witchcraft of Babylon. If she spoke, she enchained the hearts of the wise, and called down the wild goats from the crags. If she read the Koran, she would heal the heart-sick, she would give life to the girl-children buried alive; so that you would think she were gifted with the pipes of David. If she piped, Zonam would be an impostor beside her, though he was a leader in his generation. If she danced, she dislodged the turbans from men's heads; and she would make you forget the dance of the bubbles in the cups. Being possessed of her I even despised the red camels, those that are excellent and desired; with the enjoyment of her I adorned the neck of my prosperity.

I veiled her face from the rays of the sun and the moon, I excluded mention of her from my talk with strangers, fearful in case a breeze at night would betray her fragrance to others, the lightning's flash show her beauty. But through the decay of my fortune, and the malignness of my unlucky star, in the heat of wine I described her in my babbling to my neighbour. I knew that I had erred, after the arrows of my words had been shot; I begged him to keep silent about what I had uttered, and to guard my secret as one of his own. He declared that he treasured secrets as a miser hoarded dinars, and that he would not tear veils of confidence even if he were to be thrown into the fire. But not more than a day or two had passed before it occurred to the ruler of that town that he would go to the court of his Prince and pray for rain from the cloud of his bounty. He wished for a present to take with him to the Prince, that he might offer it in the course of the interview. Whereupon he began to make enquiries here and there, and be liberal in rewards to scouts, ambition being a spur to him. Then that treacherous neighbour of mine went to the Governor, and told him my secret. I knew nothing about it until his dependents rushed in upon me, and begged me to name the price for my slave, my peerless pearl, as news of her beauty had got to the ears of the Governor.

"Then sorrow overwhelmed me as the sea overwhelmed Pharaoh and his host. I tried to defend her, but there was no defence. I tried to intercede with him, but intercession was useless. My soul did not consent to part with its full moon, my heart did not consent to being torn from my breast. He gnashed his teeth at me, he shouted, he burned with anger, till at last, fearful of what would happen to me, I parted with the black eyes of my lovely one for the gold of his coin. And since then I have had a vow to God the Most High that I would never again be in the presence of a betrayer; and as glass is distinguished by this quality, that is the reason I left. Now do not blame me, since I have explained. What I have done is plain to all, surely."

Then we accepted his explanation, and kissed his cheek, and the master of the house asked Abu Zayd to sit by him, and gave him the first place on the cushion of honour. Then ten dishes of silver, on which were sweetmeats of honey and candy were brought in. These were offered to Abu Zayd by the generous host, and at first it seemed that the Seruji was going to refuse them, then taking one sweet here and another there, he said "Surely it is among the marks of good breeding that he who gives anything should give the vessel that holds it?" The host then laughed and said "By all means, have the dishes as well, and the boy who carries them to your lodging!"

Then Abu Zayd rose and thanked him very poetically, and passed the dishes round, urging us all to eat of the sweetmeats. Then when they were empty, he placed the dishes in a saddle-bag and bade us farewell, saying "I do not know if I should complain of the betrayer or thank him, whether I should forget his act or remember it, for though he was aggressive to me, yet these gifts have come to me because of the telling of that sorrowful tale."

We clustered round him, and wished to delay him, but he said "Now I should return to my cubs, and be content with what has come so easily, and not weary myself or my camels. So I must now take leave of you and commend you to the Best of Guardians." Then he mounted his riding beast and bent towards his homeward track. And when his strong camel coursed along, he left us as an assembly whose president is gone, or a night when the moon has set.

THE NINETEENTH ASSEMBLY

THE ENCOUNTER AT NASIBIN

Iraq was barren in a certain year through the failure of the stars to bring the rain-cloud; and travellers told of the tract of Nasibin, and the comfort of its wealthy people. So I mounted a camel of Mahrah, and fixed a lance at my saddle-bow and journeyed through hill and dale until I reached it.

Now, when I had halted in its fertile dwelling-place, I proposed that I would lay myself down there, and take its people for my neighbours, until the dried year should revive, and the spring rain visit the land of my family.

By Allah, my eyeball had not tasted of its sleep, my night had not travelled to its day, before I found Abu Zayd, roaming the streets of Nasibin, now stumbling with the crazed, now winning with the fortunate. From his lips he was scattering pearls. I followed him everywhere, and wherever he would gather people around him, I became his shadow.

Then there came upon him a sickness whose sharp knives bared his bone, it almost robbed him of the robe of life, so prolonged was its stay with him. Then I felt a great wrench through the loss of his presence, and the interruption of his teaching, as the suckling feels at the weaning. It was rumoured that his pledge was already forfeit, that the talons of death were fixed in him. His comrades were disturbed at the rumouring of the rumourers, and they swarmed to his courtyard, hurrying to see him as if for the last time. Bewildered, their grief, made them reel, and they beat their cheeks,

many said they were willing to give themselves and
their possessions to fate to let him live.

I was one of those who thronged the courtyard, his
inner sanctum, and his boy came to me at once, lips
parted in a smile. I enquired about the Shaykh's health
with a heavy heart, but was at once cheered by what I
heard: "He was imprisoned in the grasp of sickness but
just lately God was gracious in strengthening his last
gasp, and he recovers. So, return home, or come in and
see him, for he wants to talk again."

I was delighted at this, and though I found Abu
Zayd prostrate, yet his tongue was moving freely in
his old style. He turned his eye around upon us, and
said:

"God had saved me, praise be to Him, from a
sickness that went near to blot me out;
And He has granted me a recovery, though it must
needs be that death one day will waste me;
Death does not forget me, yet he gives me a delay
before the end of my feeding.
If it will be decreed, then will no friend avail, no, not
even the guarded domain of the Kolayb, the place of
the greatest potentate of the Nejd, could guard me
from him.
Nor care I if this day be near, or if death be put off
for a season.
For what boast is there in life?"

Then we saluted him with wishes for the lengthening
of his term and the withdrawal of his fear. We invited
each other to rise for fear of annoying him. But he
refused to let any of the visitors leave, saying "No,
please stay with me during the light of today that by
your pleasantries you may heal my sadness, for your
conversation is the food of my soul, the magnet of my
friendships." So we all tried to aim at pleasing him, and
turned to discourse. Then the time of the day-sleep
came on, and tongues were weary with talking, and it
was a hot day with fervent heat, ripening the orchards.

The invalid said "Surely drowsiness is now bending your necks and seeking your eye-corners, and he is a strenuous adversary, a suitor not to be repulsed. So make alliance with him by a day-sleep, and obey the traditions handed down." We followed willingly what he said, and we slept, and he slept, God pouring slumber on our eyelids.

We passed from the domain of Being, and woke when the heat was abated, and the day was older. Whereupon we washed hand and foot for the two mute prayers, and performed what freed us of our debt. We went to the saddling of our camels, but Abu Zayd said to his cub, who was fashioned in his likeness, "I fancy that they must now all be hungry, so bring in the Father of Assembly, the round table, and gather the guests; and serve the Father of Pleasantness, the white bread, the most delicate food of its kind; and the dish of the Father of Lovingness, the kid's flesh, with the Father of Help – salt; vegetables, and the Mother of Hospitality, the savoury dish Sikbaj; and bring wheat, the Strengthener, and the Mother of Joyfulness, that succulent pie; the Father of Loftiness, the highest-priced one, made of honey; afterwards, let them hear the Two Rumourers, the ewer and basin for washing the hands, that spread the rumour that the meal is at an end." His son did as Abu Zayd desired, and the company left their saddles and repaired to the table with much happiness. We were indeed treated to the finest of everything that was good to eat. Incense was burned all round us, as we ate and drank, and the party continued until we saw the setting of the sun.

Now as we realized that we must leave, we said to Abu Zayd "Was this not a marvellous day, though the morn was gloomy, is not the evening brilliant?" He prostrated himself in prayer, and spent a long time on his carpet, then he raised his head and said:

"Despair not in calamities of a gladdening that shall wipe away your sorrows;

For many a simoon blows, then turns to a gentle
breeze;
How many a hateful cloud arises, then blows away;
And when the smoke of the wood brings fear of the
flame, yet no blaze appears;
And often sorrow rises, and straightway sets again.
So be patient when fear assails, for time is the father
of wonders,
And hope from the peace of God blessings not to be
reckoned."

We noted down his excellent verses, and gave thanks
to the Most High; and we took leave of him at last,
glad at his recovery, overwhelmed by his bounty.

THE ENCOUNTER AT MAYYAFARIKIN

I was making towards Mayyafarikin with a number of congenial men who were not disputers, who knew nothing of dissembled hatred. And with them I was as one who does not leave his home, who travels with friends and neighbours as if he had not quitted his abode. When we had brought to their knees the camels for the halt of the night, and settled in our resting places, we agreed not to leave our own company for even the shortest time.

To our tents there came a poor beggar, bent of back and with a troubled wailing that woke us all from our slumbers, and he grew ever more shrill in his lamentation when we asked what was the matter. It seemed that he had a relative whom he could not bury as he was not able to buy him even a poor piece of cloth as a winding-sheet, so low was his condition, so meagre his state. Within a short time we had all placed a small sum of money within his palm, and I gave him a ring which I wrenched from my finger to help him further, as I felt that what I had given him was too small an amount.

He said, his eyes shining with tears "Thanks to you, who are examples even to the generous. How can it be a crime to be poor, to try to fly with only one wing? But you have done well with me. I have not asked for the gift of a province, or urged you to give the clothing of the Ka'beh, only for the shrouding of a corpse." I threw the ring to him, for I saw that it was Abu Zayd, and said "Use it for the cost of the mourning assembly!" Somehow I was sure that it was a net he had woven, one of his usual lying tales. "How noble is your deed!" he cried, "How well your flame burns!" and then he went off, running straight forward and trotting out of sight. So I went after him, till I caught him by the sleeve and said "By Allah! you will have no escape from me until you show me the shrouded corpse! Come, where is it?" He smiled sadly, then he pointed to himself, and I left him, returning to my companions, telling them what had passed between us. Then they burst into loud unsympathetic laughter, and cursed that dead man.

THE TWENTY-FIRST ASSEMBLY

THE ENCOUNTER AT RAYY AL MAHDIYEH

Being at Rayy (the birthplace of Harun al Reshid), I saw a crowd of people going to one certain spot, and someone told me there was a great preacher attracting the people there.

Ever since I began to know right from wrong I have listened to admonishings and lectures for man's betterment, so I soon arrived at the source of the fountain. There was an old bowed man, dressed in the clothes of the Dervish with hunched shoulders, and with a high-crowned *kalansuweh* cap and Persian cloak. He was preaching in a way to heal hearts and to soften rocks, so I listened.

"Son of man," he was saying, "how you cling to what harms you, how you cleave to that which deceives you! How you are attracted to that which harms you, how you are gladdened by him who flatters you, how troubled about that which wearies you but careless of that which truly concerns you. You draw wide the bow of your transgression and you robe yourself with covetousness which will destroy you in the end! You are not content with what is enough, you do not abstain from the forbidden, you will not listen to admonishing, you are not deterred by threats, and it is your habit to veer with desires. You stumble with the stumbling of the purblind beast! It is your way to labour for gain, to gather an inheritance for your heirs; though it pleases you to increase what belongs to you, yet you do not remember what is before you! You do not care whether the account be in your favour or against you, look after your two caves – the mouth and the belly – and do not think that you might be reckoned with tomorrow. Do you think that Death will take bribes? That he will distinguish between the lion and the fawn? No, by Allah, neither wealth nor children shall ward off death; and nothing profits the people of the tombs save the accepted work. Then blessing on him that hears and retains and makes good what he claims, and witholds his soul from desire, and knows that he who turns from evil is a gainer; and that man shall have nothing but his own work, and that this work shall surely be shown."

He took a short pause, then recited:

"By your life, mansions and wealth will not avail when the rich man dwells in the ground and abides in it;

So be liberal with your wealth in things pleasing to God, content with what you gain of his hire and reward;

And anticipate by it the change of Time, for he seizes with his crooked talon and his tooth;

Do not trust treacherous fortune and its deceit, for how many a lowly one it has marred and how many a noble!

But resist the desire of the soul, which no erring one ever obeyed but he fell from his high place;

And keep to the fear of God, and the dread of Him, that you may escape His punishment which is to be feared.

Do not neglect to call to mind your sin, but weep for it with tears that shall be like the rain-flood;

And bring to your mind Death and his stroke, and the terror of his meeting, and the taste of his gall-bitter cup!

For the end of the dwelling of the living is the pit

To which he shall descend, brought down from his towers.

Then well done that servant whom the evil of his

deed grieves, and who shows amendment before the shutting of the gate . . ."

Then the people gathered around showed that they were penitent, and some shed tears indeed, till the sun declined, and the day's duties were upon them. Now, there was the Prince of that region present, and when he saw that great man, a person who had some wrong done to him by a tyrannous agent began to cry his woes to the Prince. But the Prince took the part of his agent, and gave the suppliant no redress. Then in despair the unfortunate one appealed to the Dervish to say something in his defence, as he was inarticulate.

So up got the preacher and addressed the multitude like this:

"Wonderful! A man hoping to attain to rule, and then when he attains his desires he wrongs;

He weaves warp and woof in tyrannies; now lapping at their will, now bidding others to lap;

Nor cares he, when he is following his desires in them, whether he maintains his religion or destroys it;

O woe to him! If he knew well that there is no state that does not change, surely he would not transgress;

Or if he saw clearly what is the repentance of him who inclines his hearing to the lie of informers, he would not incline it;

But obey him whose hand is in possession of the leading-cord, cast down your eye if he neglects observance or speaks vainly;

And graze on bitter pasture when he calls you to the grazing on it, and water at the salt well when he forbids you the sweet,

And bear his injury even though its touch afflicts you, and pour out your flood of tears; no, exhaust it;

For fortune shall give you the laugh of him when it departs from him, and kindles for the ambush against him the fire of war.

It shall bring down on him exultation, when he appears vacant of his office, emptied of it;

And you shall be sorry for him when his cloak lies soiled in the dust of shame.

That is his fate; and then surely he shall one day stand in the place where even the master of eloquence shall be found a lisper;

And he shall be gathered to judgement viler than the toadstool of the plain; he shall be reckoned with for his shortcomings and excess;

And he shall be chastised for that which he has committed, and for him whom he has chosen; he shall be demanded of for what he sipped and what he supped.

And he shall be reckoned with concerning small things, as he was wont to do with mankind, but more thoroughly.

So that he shall bite his hand at his governing, and wish that he had not sought from it what he sought."

Then he said "O you who are belted with authority, and trained to rule, put away your wantonness at your dominion, and vain trusting in your might. For dominion is a breeze that changes and power is a lightning that deceives. And truly the happiest of rulers is he whose people are happy with him, and the most wretched in both worlds is he whose ruling is ill. Then do not be as one who neglects the life to come, abjectly disregarding it, who loves the fleeting life and seeks it, who wrongs the people and afflicts them, and who, when he bears rule, walks in the earth to do violence in it. By Allah, the Judge shall not be unregarding, you shall not be left at large, O man; but the balance will be set for you, and as you reward, so shall you be rewarded."

Then the Governor was sullen at what he heard, and his colour changed. He began to groan concerning his rule, and followed sigh with sigh. Then he attended to the complainer, and rid him of his complaint, and rebuked the one that was complained of. He was most courteous to the preacher, and gave him gifts, and urged him to visit him. The wronged man departed victorious, and the wronger was checked. Then the preacher went forth swaggering among his comrades, glorying in his success. But I followed him, and showed him a sharp glance from the eye of reproof. When he was aware that I was turning my face to him, he said "The better of two guides is he that leads aright." Then he came near to me and recited:

"I am he whom you know, Harith,
The talker with kings, the wit, the intimate.
I charm as charms a brother of earnestness, at times a jester.
Events have not changed me since I first met you,
Nor has the vexing calamity peeled my branch;
Nor has any splitting edge cloven my tooth;
But my claw is fixed in every prey,
On each herd that roams my wolf is ravaging;
So that it is as though I were the heir of all mankind,
Their Shem, their Ham, their Japhet."

Then I said "By Allah, now you are surely Abu Zayd, but you rival Amr ibn Obayd, the celebrated ascetic of the time of Khalif Al Mansur!" and I saw that this pleased him.

In parting he said to me "Keep to truth though it scorch you with the fire of threatening; and seek to please God, for the most foolish of mankind is he who angers the master and pleases the slave." He took leave of his fellows, and departed, trailing his sleeves. We searched for him afterwards in Rayy, but no one could find him, or could learn what locust had gone off with him.

THE TWENTY-SECOND ASSEMBLY

THE ENCOUNTER OF THE EUPHRATES

During a time of quiet, I betook myself to the water-lands of the Euphrates, and there I met with some scribes, more pleasant in their manners than the sweet waters. I joined myself to them for their culture, not their gold, and I accompanied them because of their scholarship, not their banquets. Among them I sat with equals of Al Ka'ka, son of Showr, (a man of the Arabs famous for his generosity, and reckoned with Hatim Tai and Ka'b ibn Mameh) and with them I attained to plenty after want.

Then they made me sharer in food and dwelling, and set me above themselves, as the finger tip is above the finger. They made me the son of their intimacy and the treasurer of their secrets in time of office and leisure. Now it happened that they were called to visit for official purposes the corn lands of the villages, and they took me with them by boat. When we had settled on our cushions in that black-sailed one, and started to glide through the water, we found there an old man, dressed in a threadbare coat and worn turban, whom several of us were anxious to turn away. But when we saw that he was so wretched, and praised God after sneezing, we left him alone, and even silenced him when he began to address us. There he sat, speechless, looking at the pass he had reached, and waiting for the help which comes to the wronged.

We roamed conversationally through the by-ways of the serious and the gay, until we got to mention of two kinds of official writing, in which all joined enthusiastically. One said that the scribes of Composition were the finest, while another leaned to the preferring of Accountants; and the arguing grew sharp, and the dispute grew lengthy. Suddenly the old disreputable-looking man said: "My friends, you have made much clamour, and adduced the true and the mistaken, but the clear decision rests with me, so be content with my intervention, and consult no one after me. Know that the art of Composition is the more lofty, though the art of Accounts may be the more useful. The pen of correspondence is the choice orator, but the pen of account-keeping picks up phrases carelessly; and the fablings of eloquence are copied to be studied, but the ledgers of accounts are soon blotted out and razed. The composer is the Postbag of Secrets, the confidant of the mighty, the greatest among guests; his pen is the tongue of sovereignty, and the knight of the skirmish; it carries good news, and it warns, and it is the intercessor and the envoy. By it fortresses are won, and foes are vanquished, and the rebel is made obedient, and the distant is brought near. Its master is free from suits, secure from the malice of accusers, praised in the assemblies, not exposed to the drawing up of registers."

Now when in his judgement he had arrived at this point, he saw from the glances of the company that he had sowed love and hatred, and that he had pleased a part and angered a part. So he followed up his discourse by saying: "Not but that the Art of Composing is founded on fabrication, for the pen of the Accountant holds firm, but the pen of the Composer stumbles. And between taking tribute by the impost on transactions and the reading of the leaves of volumes, is a difference to which comparison cannot apply, into which doubt cannot enter; for tribute fills purses, but reading empties the head. The tax of the memorandum book enriches the overseer, but the interpretation of rolls wearies the eye. Then also the Accountants are the guardians of wealth, the bearers of burdens, the truthful relaters, the trustworthy envoys, the guides in doing justice and obtaining it, the sufficing witnesses in breach of contract. Of their number is the Minister of Finance, who is the Hand of the Prince, the Pivot of the Council, the balance of business, the overseer of the agents. To him is the reference in peace and war, on him is the management in revenue and expenditure; by him hang evil and advantage; in his hand is the rein of giving and denying. Were it not for the pen of Accountants, the fruit of learning would perish, and fraud would endure to the Day of Judgement. The order of transactions would be loosened; the wound of wrongs would be unavenged; the neck of just-dealing would be fettered – the sword of wrong-doing would be drawn. Moreover, the pen of composition fables, but the pen of accounting interprets. The Accountant is a close scrutinizer, the Composer is an *abu barakish* (the bird of gaudy and changing plumage) yet each, when he rises high, has his venom until he be met and charmed; and in what each produces there is vexing till he can be visited and bribed; save those that work righteously – how few are they!"

When he had this way supplied us with what was pure and good, we asked him of his lineage; but he shrank from telling it, and if he had been able to escape he would have done so. Then I was sad because of his secrecy, but after a while I recollected him, and an instant later I said "Now by Him who controls the rolling heavens and the voyaging ships, surely I catch the breeze of Abu Zayd, though once I knew him lord of comeliness and vigour." He smiled, laughing at my speech, and said: "Yes, I am he, though with a change in state and strength." Whereupon I said to my companions: "This is he, who can fashion words as no one else can fashion them, who cannot be vied with."

Then they courted his friendship, and offered him wealth, but he declined, and would not accept anything, and he said: "Since you have hurt my honour on account of my worn garments, and cast a shadow on my soul for the threadbareness of my coat, I will look upon you with a heated eye, you shall only have from me a shipmate's companionship."

Then he said

"Hear, my brother, commandment from a counsellor who does not mingle his purity of counsel with deceit;

Do not hasten with a decisive judgement in the praise of him whom you have not tried, nor in rebuke of him;

But stay in your judgement on him till you have had a view of his two characters in his two conditions of content and anger;

And until his deceiving flash be distinguished from his truthful one by those who watch it, and his flood from his light rain;

And then if you perceive what dishonours him, hide it generously, but if you see what becomes him, publish it:

And whoso deserves to be exalted, exalt him; and whoso deserves abasement, abase him to the sewer;

Know that the pure gold in the vein of the earth is hidden till it is brought out by digging;

And the worth of the dinar, its secret appears by scratching it, and not from the beauty of the graving.

It is folly that you should magnify the ignorant by reason of the brightness of his dress or the splendour of his adorning;

Or that you should make little of the man who is refined in soul on account of the threadbareness of his garb, or the shabbiness of his furniture,

For how many an owner of two torn mantles is reverenced for his worth, and he that is striped in his garments has ill-fame through his baseness;

For when a man approaches not to infamy, then only are his rags the steps to his throne.

It does not hurt the sword that its sheath is worn,
Nor the hawk that its nest is mean."

Then he asked the sailors to stop, and put him off. Each of us repented that we had been so careless to him, and we vowed that we would never again slight a man for the raggedness of his garments, and that we would not despise the sword that was hidden in the sheath, however ancient it might be.

THE TWENTY-THIRD ASSEMBLY

THE ENCOUNTER OF THE PRECINCT

During the days of my prime, I found my home was becoming irksome to me, so I left, and made haste by horse to another place. I went by rough roads which no steps had smoothed, until I came to the domain of the Khalifate, and the sanctuary which guards men from fear. Then I put off that sense of dread and its conception which I had had with me, and robed myself in the raiment of security and its vest. I went forward one day to exercise my steed in the Precinct, and to feast my eyes upon its beauties. Then I was surprised to see there horsemen who followed each other, and men on foot who swarmed, and one old man long of tongue but short of cloak, who led by the collar a fresh-faced youth in a worn tunic.

So I spurred on the track of the spectators till we reached the gate of the Prefecture. There was the Master of Protection sitting squarely on his seat, awing all by his very deportment.

Then the old man said to him "God Magnify the Governor, and set his foot on high! Know that I bred this youth from a suckling, and brought him up, as he was an orphan, and spent years instructing him. But now that he is shrewd and strong, he has bared and brandished the sword of emnity. Since by me he was watered and made fruitful I never thought that he would be so perverse towards me."

"On what offence of mine have you hit, that you say things like this about me in public?" cried the young man. "For, by Allah, I have not covered the face of your kindness, I have not rent the veil of your secret; I have not broken the staff of your estate; I have not disregarded giving thanks to you."

"Woe to you," responded the old man. "What guilt is fouler than yours, what vice more base than yours? For you have claimed my magic and appropriated it; you have stolen my poetry! Now among poets the stealing of poetry is more shameful than the stealing of white silver and yellow gold; and their jealousy over the daughters of their wits is as the jealousy over virgin daughters."

The Governor said to the old man "When he stole, did he flay, or transform, or copy?" The old man answered "Now by Him who made poetry the register of the Arabs and the interpreter of scholarship, he did nothing less than dock the completeness of its exposition, and make foray on two thirds of its flock."

"Recite the verses altogether," said the Governor, "that it can be shown what he took from you."

Then the old man began:

"O you who court the base world, know that it is a net of destruction, a pool of impurities;
A habitation which, when it makes you laugh today, makes you weep tommorow; away with such a habitation!
When its clouds overshadow, no thirst is refreshed by them, for they are a dry cloud which deceives;
Its forays do not cease, nor is one prisoner even ransomed by the mightiest of stakes;
Towards how many a one, made wanton by false confidence in it, until he has shown himself as one overstepping in power,
Has it turned the back of the shield, and made its blade to lap of his blood, and leaped to the taking of revenge!
So keep guard on your life, in case it should pass away lost in the world, left astray with no protection:

And cut the bonds of your love for the world and your seeking of it; so you shall find right guidance and comfort of the inner parts,

And when it makes a truce from its stratagem, be on your watch against the warring of enemies, and the assault of the treacherous;

And know that its calamities come suddenly, even though the goal is far, and the journeys of the fates be tardy."

The Governor said "And how did the lad then?" So the old man recited, saying "Now you can see how he has copied me, it was my very own idea!

"O you who court the world of baseness, know that it is a net of destruction,

A habitation, which, if it makes you laugh today, makes you weep tomorrow.

When its clouds overshadow, no thirst is refreshed by them,

Its forays do not cease, nor is its prisoner ransomed,

Towards how many a one made wanton by false confidence in it, until he has shown himself contumacious,

Has it turned the back of the shield, and made its blade lap his blood!

So keep guard on your life in case it passes away, lost in the world, left astray;

And cut the bonds for your love of the world, and your seeking for it, and you shall find the right guidance.

And when it makes a truce from its stratagem, be on your watch against the warring of enemies,

And know that its calamities come suddenly even though the goal is far."

The Governor, hearing this, turned to the boy and said "Perdition upon you for a rebellious disciple and a thieving pupil!"

"May I remain aloof from scholarship and its sons!" rejoined the young man, "May I be joined to whoever is adverse to it, and breaks down its edifices! It only shows that our thoughts came together as the same hoof often falls on the hoofprint. These verses of mine came to me long before I heard his, I swear it!"

The Governor thought that the best way to test them would be to hold an immediate contest of wits, so that he could distinguish the genius from the fool, so he said, "If you wish for the manifestation of the true from the false, for the exposure of him that lacks, do you now alternate in verse-completing, so that by clear proof he who perishes may perish, and he who lives, lives." They said to him with one tongue "We agree, so give us your command."

He said "Of all kinds of eloquence, I am fondest of the kind which strings ten verses upon a single string; weave then together, and embroider with your wit. And put in verse the tale of my condition concerning a mistress of mine, who is rare of form, dark red of lip, graceful in undulation, but full of pride and fault-finding, given to feign forgetfulness of argument, and to prolong denial, and to break promises, while I am her slave."

Then the two began to race each other line by line, until the series of verses was perfected and made up:

Old Man: "There is a ruddy-lipped one who has encompassed my enslaving by the delicacy of her utterance, and left me with the companion of sleeplessness by perfidiousness."

Youth: "She has assayed to slay me by her aversion; truly I am in her bond, since she has got my heart completely."

Old Man: "I give faith to her falsehood for fear of her turning from me; I am content to listen to her folly through dread that she should fly me."

Youth: "I deem her tormenting to be sweet; and as often as she renews my torment, the love of being kindly to her is renewed in me."

Old Man: "She is forgetful of duty, and to forget is a

fault; she angers my heart – the heart which guards her secret."

Youth: "What is most wonderful in her is the glorying of her vanity; yet I do make too much of her for me to speak to her of her pride."

Old Man: "From me she has praise sweet of fragrance; but my lot from her is a folding-up of love after its out-spreading."

Youth: "O, if she were just, she would not be fault-finding, but she wrongs me; another, and not I, gathers the dew of her mouth."

Old Man: "Were it not for her graceful motion I would turn my rein in haste to another, the light of whose full moon I might look upon."

Youth: "But notwithstanding the discordance between her and me, I hold the bitter as sweet through my docility to her command."

Now, when in alternation they had recited these lines to the Governor, he was amazed at the wit of the two so justly balanced. He said "I testify before God that you are like one pair of fire-staves in a case. Now, this youth spends what God has given him, through his own wealth he is independent of another. So, old man, repent of your suspicion of him, and turn again to honouring him."

"Far be it from me that my love should return to him," said the old man, "or that my confidence should either, for I have proved his ingratitude for kindness, I have been tried by him with shameful revolt."

But the lad interrupted him and said "O friend, you know that contention is ill-luck, and spite meanness; to hold suspicion as truth is a sin; to vex the innocent is wrong. Granted that I have committed an offence and a crime, remember what you yourself recited to me in the season of familiarity?

'Pardon your brother when he mingles his right aiming with error,

And shrink from rebuking him if he swerves or

declines:

Keep to your kind dealing towards him whether he thanks the kindness or slights it;

Be obedient when he revolts, be lowly when he magnifies himself; draw near to him when he goes away from you.

Keep faith with him even though he fails in what you and he have stipulated,

And know that if you seek a perfect man you desire beyond bounds.

Who is there who has never done ill? Who is there whose deed is always fair?

Do you not see the loved and the hated linked together in one class,

As the thorn comes forth on the branches with the fruit that is gathered.

And the delight of long life has mingled with it the trouble of hoariness.' "

Then the old man darted his tongue as the serpent does, and his eye was hawklike as he spoke. "By Him who has adorned the heavens with fire, and sent down water from the clouds, truly my declining from reconciliation is from fear of ignominy. For this lad has been fed by me, looked after in all his affairs, and when fortune was plenteous, I was not niggardly to him. But, as for now, the time is frowning, the contents of life are a misery, so this my garb is a loan, and not even a mouse approaches my house."

Then the Governor's heart grew tender, and he was most sympathetic towards them both. He was much inclined now to help them, and he asked the other onlookers to withdraw.

Now, I had been gazing on the face of the old man, and try as I might, the crowd got in the way of my seeing him clearly, so that I could not get near enough to prove my suspicions. But when the crowd disappeared, I was able to approach him, and it was indeed Abu Zayd, and the lad was his son.

But he stopped me with a signal of his hand, and so I stopped swooping upon him, though I dearly wanted to go to him. The Governor was saying "What is your wish, and where are you staying?" "With my friend, the owner of my clothes," said the old man.

The Governor was pleased to allow me to sit near, and permitted me to listen to everything which passed. I saw him give two robes of honour to the father and son, and he presented them with a large sum of money. He stipulated that they should live in kindness together until the coming of the Day of Fear. Then they rose up from his presence, lifting their voices in thanks for his benefits.

I followed that I might know where they were staying, and that I might supply myself from their talk. When we had come away from the house of the Governor, one of his guards overtook me and said that His Excellency had recalled me to his Court. I said to Abu Zayd, whom I had just taken by the sleeve, "What shall I say to him if he asks me what I have thought about the proceedings we have just witnessed? I am sure that he is sending for me that he should question me."

Said Abu Zayd "Show him the folly of his heart; and how I have played with his understanding, that he may know that his breeze has met with a whirlwind, that his stream has encountered the deep."

I replied "I fear that his anger may be kindled, so that his blaze might scorch you, or his caprice might quicken, that his violence might come on you."

He said "I am just setting off for Arroha, (Edessa) and how should the great star Sohayle (Canopus) and Soha (the smallest star in the tail of the Great Bear) meet?"

THE TWENTY-FOURTH ASSEMBLY

THE ENCOUNTER CALLED 'OF THE PORTION'

This Assembly contains the "grammatical riddles" of which the author speaks in his preface. Abu Zayd, falling into the company of some refined persons who are amusing themselves in the suburbs of Bagdad, is at first despised by them for the shabbiness of his garb. But the recitation of a singer causes the conversation to turn upon the famous and never-ending controversy concerning the use of the *raf'* and the *nasb,* or, in European terminology, the nominative and accusative case, in certain Arabic phrases. The company plunge into the dispute with all the ardour which never failed to be kindled by grammatical disquisitions; and when they can come to no agreement, Abu Zayd interposes, and gives his opinion. As they do not accept it readily, and attempt to argue with him, he at once reduces them to submission by proposing twelve enigmas, involving abstruse and technical points of Arabic grammar. No one can solve them; and Abu Zayd refuses to gratify their curiosity by giving an explanation until each one of them has made him a present. Then he leaves them, refusing to drink with them on the ground that in his declining age he had made a vow against wine. The answers are briefly given in an appendix from the pen of Hariri himself.

I was in company in the portion of Ar Rabi, in the season of spring, with youths whose faces were brighter than its lights, whose dispositions were more goodly than its flowers, whose utterances were more delicate than the air of its dawns. And through them I looked upon what would shame the flowering spring and suffice for the sounds of lutes. And we had taken oath together for the guarding of affection and the forbidding of self-seeking; and that no one of us should hold aloof in enjoyment, or keep to himself even the smallest pleasure.

Now we had agreed together on a day whose mist had risen, whose beauty was growing, whose light cloud bade to the morning draught, that we would amuse ourselves by going forth to one of the meadows, to pasture our eyes on the shining plots, and polish our minds by a forecasting of the rains; so we sallied forth, and we were as the months in number, and as the two boon-companions of Jathimeh in affection, to a garden which had assumed its gilding and adorned itself, whose flowers were various in their kinds and hues; And with us were the headstrong ruddy wine, and cup-bearers like suns; and the singer who charms the hearer and delights him, who feasts each hearing with what it covets.

Now when we had fully taken seat, and the cups were circling to us, there intruded on us a sharp fellow, on him was an old coat: and we frowned on him as frown the soft damsels on the gray-heads, and we felt that the purity of our day was now troubled. But he greeted with the greeting of the intelligent; and taking seat he opened perfume-vials of prose and verse; but we shrank from his expansion, and hastened to roll up what he spread out; until chanted our rare singer, our charming modulator:

How long, Su'ad, wilt thou not join my cord, nor pity me for what I meet with?

I have been patient with thee until my patience is overcome, until my spirit has almost reached my throat.

But come! I am resolved to do myself right, drinking thereby to my mistress as she drinks to me;

For if union (*was-lan*) please her — then union (*was-lun*); but if rupture — then rupture like a very divorce.

Then we asked the player on the double-twisted

strings why he *nasbed* the first *wasl* and *raf'ed* the second. And he swore by the tomb of his parents that he had spoken as Sibawayh preferred. But the opinions of the company were divided as to the admissibility of the *nasb* and *raf*. And a section said, "The *raf* of both, that is correct;" and a part said, "Nothing is lawful but the state of *nasb*;" while to the rest the answer was impracticable, and the clamouring kindled among them. But that intruder showed the smilingness of one who knows a matter, though he spoke not a single word.

However, when the cries were still, and the scolded and the scolder were silent, he said, "O people, I will announce to you its interpretation, I will distinguish the sound phrase from the sick. Verily the *raf* and the *nasb* of each *wasl* are lawful, and an interchange of the inflection between them; and that is according to what is left understood, and to the virtual signification which is elided in this puzzle."

Then was the company reckless in hastening to dispute with him, and in gliding into contention with him. But he said: "Well, since ye call to me to 'Come down', and ye gird yourselves for the war:

What is the word which, as ye will, is a particle that is loved, or the name of that which contains the slender milch-camel?

And what is the noun which alternates between a singular that binds, and a plural that clings?

And what is the *h* which, when it attaches itself, takes away heaviness and loosens the bound?

And where does the *sin* enter and depose the regent without courtesy?

And what is that which is always *mansub* as a term of circumstance, while only a particle makes it *makhfud*?

And what is the annexed noun which lacks one of the handles of annexion, and whose power varies between evening and morning?

And what is the regent whose last joins his first, and whose reverse effects what he effects?

And what is the regent whose deputy is more spacious than he in abode, and greater in craft, and more frequent in mention of God Most High?

And in what place do males put on the veils of women, and the ladies of the alcoves go forth with the turbans of men?

And where is the keeping of ranks necessary to the struck and the striker?

And what is the noun which gives no sense except by the addition to it of two words, or the shortening of it to two letters; and in the first case there is adhesion, and in the second compulsion?

And what is the epithet which, when it is followed by *nun,* he to whom it is applied lessens in men's eyes, and is set low in reputation, and is reckoned among the simpletons, and exposes himself to dishonour?

Now these are twelve questions to match your number, to balance your disputatiousness; if ye add, I add; if ye return, I return.

Now from these his riddles, which terrified as they poured, there came on our thoughts bewilderment and barrenness. And when it baffled us to swim in his sea, and our talismans had yielded to his enchantment, we changed from weariness in looking at him to the seeking of instruction from him, and from the wrong of being annoyed by him to the desire of learning of him.

But he said, "Now by Him who has sent down grammar into speech to be as salt in food, and has veiled its risings from the perceptions of the vulgar, I will not give you a wish, I will not heal for you a pain, unless every hand endow me, and each of you distinguish me by a gift."

Then remained not one in the company but was obedient to his command, and cast to him the hidden treasure of his sleeve. And when he had got it under his wallet-string he kindled the flame of his genius. And then did he disclose of the secrets of his riddles and of the wonders of his puzzling, that wherewith he cleared away the rust from our understandings, that whose rising he manifested by the light of proof. And we were astonished when we understood, and we wondered when we were answered, and we repented over what had escaped from us. And we began to excuse ourselves with the excusing of the sagacious; and we offered to him the quaffing of the wine-cup.

But he said, "Need is not courtesy; and as for drinking, there remains in it no sweetness for me." Then he turned up his face morosely, and plucked away his side scornfully, and recited:

Gray hair forbids me that wherein are my joys; how then should I bring together the wine and my hands' palms?

Is the morning draught of the old wine lawful, now that the hoariness of my head lights up my morning?

I swear that wine shall never again blend with me as long as my breath cleaves to my body, and my words to my speech;

That my hand shall not deck itself with the cups of must; that I will not turn round my lot among the goblets;

That I will not set my thought to the mixed drink; that I will not go joyfully to the wine;

That I will not gather myself to the wine cooled of the north wind; that I will choose no companion, save the sober.

Hoariness blots out my merriment when he writes upon my head; hated be he for a blotting scribe!

He shines forth to blame my turning the reins to pleasure; away with him for one who shines forth but to blame!

Now were I wanton while my temple is hoary, then would my lamp be put out among the lamps of Ghassan,

A people whose disposition is the honouring of their guests; and gray hair is a guest to whom honour is due, my friend.

Then he slipped away as slips the serpent, and sped with the speeding of the cloud. And I knew then that he was the light of Seruj; the full moon of scholarship that passes through the signs of heaven. And our end was grief at his departure and separation after he was gone.

Explanation of the Arabic subtleties and grammatical riddles which are contained in this Assembly:

As for the first part of the last verse of the song, namely – *Fa'in was-lan alathou bihi fa was-lun,* (if union please her, then union), it is like the phrase *Wa in sharran fa sharrun, Al mar'u mujzzi bi amalihi in khairan fa khairun* (Man is rewarded according to his work; if good, good, if evil, evil.) Now Sibawayh introduced this question into his Book, and allowed four modes of inflecting it. The first and best is that you should *nasb* the first *khair* and *raf'* the second, *nasb* the first *sharr* and *raf'* the second. Then would the virtual meaning be, "If his work be good then his reward is good; and if his work be evil, then his reward is evil;" for the first is *nasbed* through being the predicate of *kana*, and the second is *raf'ed* through being the predicate of an elided inchoative. And in this mode, *kana* and its noun are elided, because the conditional particle *in* (if) points to their virtual presence; and the inchoative is also elided, because the *fa*, which is the answer to the condition, points to it; and that is by reason that an inchoative commonly follows *fa*. The second mode is that you should *nasb* both; and then the virtual meaning of the sentence is, "If his wish be good, then he is rewarded good; and if his wish be evil, then he is rewarded evil." Here the first is *nasbed,* because it is the predicate of *kana*, and the second is *nasbed* as the object of the verb's action. The third mode is that you should *raf'* both; then the virtual sense of the sentence is, "If there be good in his work, then his reward is good; and the first *khair* is *raf'ed* because it is the noun of *kana*, and the second is *raf'ed* because it is the predicate of an elided inchoative; as was shown in the exposition of the first mode. And it may be that the first *khair* is *raf'ed* through being the *agent* of *kana;* and that the *kana,* which receives a virtual power here, is the complete attributive verb, with the meaning "exists", or "occurs"; which would need no predicate, as in the phrase of God Most High, "If he *be* one in difficulty". Then the virtual meaning in the example would be, "If good *be,* then the reward is good": that is, "If good exists, then the reward is good". The fourth and weakest mode is that you should *raf* the first on the principle explained in the third case, and *nasb* the second on that which was mentioned in the second case. Then the virtual meaning will be, "If there be good in his work, then he is rewarded good". According to this interpretation, and by the use of the virtually understood words which are here elided, runs the inflection of the verse sung in the Assembly. And among expressions of the same kind is the sentence, "The man was killed by what he killed with; if a sword, a sword; if a knife, a knife".

Now as to the word which is a particle that is loved, or the name of that which contains the slender milch camel; it is *naam.* If you use it to admit the truth of what is told you, or to promise in answer to a request, then it is a particle: but if you mean by it "camels", then it is a noun: and *naam* is masculine and feminine, and is a general name for camels, and for all cattle (in which last definition camels are comprised). And among camels is comprised the *harrf;* which means a slender she-camel. She is called *harrf,* from being likened to the *harrf* (edge) of a sword. But it is also said that the word means a stout she-camel, through the likening of her to the *harrf* (ridge) of a mountain.

As for the noun which alternates between a singular that binds and a plural that clings, it is *sarawil* (trousers or drawers). Some say that this is a singular form, and that its plural is *sarawilat*; and according to this opinion, it is a singular; and from its being gathered round the waist, he gives it the epithet of "binding". Others say, "Nay, it is a plural, and its singular form is *sirwel*"; and, according to this opinion, it is a plural; and the meaning of the expression "clings" is, that it is not *fully declined*. Now, the reason that this kind of plural is not fully declined (and it consists of every plural whose third letter is an *elif* followed by a strengthened letter, or by two letters, or by three letters, the middle one of which is quiescent), is on account of its heaviness, and its divergence from the other plurals, inasmuch as there is no form like it among the singular nouns. And in this riddle he gives the epithet "clinging" to that which is not fully declined.

As for the *h*, which, when it attaches itself, takes away heaviness, and loosens the bound; it is the *h* which is affixed to the form of plural above mentioned; as in *sayarifah* (bankers), *sayakirah* (polishers); for this form of plural becomes fully declined when the *h* is affixed to it; because the *h* changes it to the form of singular nouns like *rafahiyah* and *karahiyah;* and it is thus lightened, and becomes declinable. And in this riddle he gives to that which is not fully declined the epithet of "bound", as in the former he gave it the epithet of "clinging".

As for the *sin*, which deposes the regent without courtesy, it is that which is prefixed to the future verb, and divides it from *an*, which, before the prefixion, was one of the *instruments of nasbing*. The verb is then *raf' ed,* and the *an* is changed from being a *nasber* to the verb, to being the lightened *an*, used in the place of the heavy. Thus, in the sentence of God, Praise be to Him, *'alima anna sayakuna minkum muradha* (He knows that there shall be sick among you), the virtual reading is *'alima annahu sayakuna*.

Now as to that which is *nasbed,* as a term of circumstance, while only a particle *khafds* it, it is *'inda,* which
is never *jerred* in choice speech, except by *min;* for the
vulgar expression, *thahabtu ili 'indihi,* is a mistake.

As to the annexed noun, which is deprived of one of
the handles of annexion, and whose power varies
between evening and morning; it is *ladan.* For this is
one of the nouns which necessarily require annexion,
and whatever noun follows it is *jerred* by it, except
ghudwa; for the Arabs make this *mansub* after *ladan,*
through the frequency with which they use it in
discourse: they also *nunnate* it, that it may fully appear
that it is *mansub,* and that it is not one of the class of
jerred nouns which are not fully declinable. Among
some of the grammarians, *ladan* has the same meaning
as *'anda;* but the correct view is that there is a delicate
difference between them; namely that the meaning of
'anda applies to whatever is in your possession or
power, whether it be near to you or at a distance, while
ladan applies only to what is in your presence and
close to you.

And as for the regent, whose last joins his first, and
whose reverse effects what he effects; it is *yaa,* the
reverse of which is *ary;* and both are among the
particles of calling; and the effect of both upon the
noun of the person called to is the same, although *yaa*
circulates more in discourse, and is of more frequent
usage. Some, however, prefer that a person who is near
should be called to with *ai* only, as he is called to with
hamzeh.

As for the regent whose deputy is more spacious
than he in abode, and greater in craft, and more
frequent in mention of God Most High, it is the *be* of
swearing. This *be* is the original particle of swearing; as
is shown by its being used when the verb of swearing is
expressed, as when you say *uksimi billah* (I swear by
God); and by its being prefixed also to the pronoun; as
when you say *bik liafallana* (By Thee, I will do it).

Afterwards the *wa* was substituted for it in the oath, because they are both labial letters, and also on account of the relationship of their meanings; since the *wa* gives the sense of union, and the *be* that of adhesion, and the two meanings approach each other. Then the *wa*, which was substituted for the *be*, became more common in speech, and was more largely applied in forms of swearing; and for this reason he riddles that it is more frequent in mention of God Most High. Also the *wa* is larger in dwelling than the *be*, because the *be* is prefixed only to the noun, and effects nothing but the *jerr*; while the *wa* is prefixed to the noun, and the verb, and the particle, and sometimes it *jerrs with the oath,* and sometimes by understanding *rubba*, and it is also ranked with the *nasbers of the verb,* and with the *instruments of conjunction,* and for this reason he describes it by spaciousness of abode, and greatness of cunning.

And as for the place where males put on the veils of women, and the ladies of the alcoves go forth with the turbans of men; it is the first degree of the numeral, when in the state of annexion; namely, the numerals between three and ten, for they have *te* in the masculine, and are without it in the feminine, as in the phrase of Him Most High, *sakharha 'alaihim sab'i layalin wa thamaniyati ayamin husouman* (He compelled it upon them seven nights and eight days consecutively); while everywhere else the *te* is one of the distinctives of the feminine. You see how the rule of masculine and feminine is reversed in this case; so that each turns to a form that is not its own, and goes forth in the garb of the other.

As to the place where the keeping of ranks is necessary to the struck and the striker; it is when there is ambiguity between the agent and the patient, through the sign of inflection failing to be openly expressed in both or one of them. This takes place when they are both *maksur*, like *Mousa* or *aisa*; or belong to the nouns of indication, like *thaka* and *hatha*. In such cases it is necessary, for the avoiding of ambiguity, that each of the two nouns should be kept in its proper order; so that the agent may be known by its coming first, and the patient by its following after.

As for the noun which gives no sense except by the addition to it of two words, or the shortening of it to two letters, it is *mahma* (whatever). About this word there are two opinions: one that it is compounded of *mah* which means "stop", and of *maa*; the second, and the correct one, is that the root of the word is *maa*, to which another *maa* was added augmentively, as it is to *in*, so that the utterance became *maa maa*. But the succession of two words with the same utterance became troublesome to people, and they substituted *he* for the first *elif*, so that the two became *mahmaa*. This word is one of the *instruments of condition and compensation,* and when you utter it the sentence is not completed, and the meaning is not seized, except by the addition of two words after it, as "Whatever you do I will do," so that it necessarily "adheres" to a verb. But if you shorten it to the two letters *mah*, meaning "stop", then the meaning is intelligible, and in that case you "compel" him you are addressing to stop.

And as for the epithet which, when it is followed by *nun*, he to whom it is applied lessens in men's eyes, and is set low, and is reckoned among the simpletons, and exposes himself to dishonour; it is *dhaif* (a guest), which, when *nun* is added to it, changes to *dhaifanu*, which means one who intrusively follows the guest, and who is set down as base coin when he is tested.

THE TWENTY-FIFTH ASSEMBLY

THE ENCOUNTER AT KEREJ

I was wintering in Kerej (between Ispahan and Hamadan) by reason of the fact that I was there for the repayment of a debt, and I experienced its fierce winter and its scorching cold, that which afflicted me with sorest torment.

I sat as long as I could beside my fire, and did not venture out except for some necessity, until one day I had to go to a certain place on business. I saw in the street a large crowd, surrounding a poor old man, who in all that cold, was almost bare; he was turbanned with a kerchief, and had just a small piece of linen around his loins.

However, he was reciting, and these were his words:
"O people, nothing can announce to you my poverty
More truly than this, my nakedness in the season of cold.
So from my outward misery, judge the inward condition, and what is hidden of my state;
And be aware of a change in the truce of fortune;
For know that I was once illustrious of rank,
I had command of plenty, and of a blade that severed;
My yellow gold served my friends, and my lances destroyed my foes;
Then, my habitation was razed, my camels' milk-flow delayed,
My price and my song went down among men,
And I became the lean beast of poverty and need,
Naked of back, stripped of my covering,

As though I were a spindle in my nakedness.

Now, is there anyone here who is a deep sea of bounty, lord of an ample robe,

Who will cloak me either with embroidered garment or ragged coat,

Seeking the face of God, and not my thanks?"

Then he added "O you lords of wealth who trail in furred robes, he that is endowed with good let him expend; he that is able to bestow, let him bestow. For the world is a treacherous place, and fortune trips; ability is the visit of a vision, and opportunity is a summer cloud. For, by Allah, I have often met with its winter, and prepared its necessities before its coming. But today, sirs, my arm is my pillow, my skin is my garment, the hollow of my hand is my dish. So let him that is wise consider my estate, and be beforehand with the changing of the nights, for the happy man is he who takes warning of his fellow, and makes preparation for his journey."

"You have certainly displayed your scholarship," said one, "Now tell us your pedigree."

"A curse on him who boasts of mouldering bones!" said he, "There is no glory but in piety and choice scholarship. By your life, man is but the son of his own day, according as that day displays itself, he is not the son of his yesterday. There is no boast in rotten bones; there is only the glory of him who seeks glory through himself."

Then he sat down, and shrank, shivering, and said "O God, who overwhelm with Your Bounty, and have asked us to ask You, send Your blessings on Mohammed and his House, and help me against the terrors of the cold; and appoint some generous man who shares even though it be only a scrap." So, when he had thus disclosed himself, the glances of my eye began to test him. I saw that it was Abu Zayd, and that his going naked was but a noose for his prey.

He realized that I had recognized him, and avoided

my face, saying further: "I swear by the shade of night and the moon, by the stars and the moonlight, that no one shall cloak me but one whose disposition is worthy, whose face is imbued with the dew of benevolence."

I was grieved at his shivering, so I took off the fur coat that was my plumage by day and my covering by night, and gave it to him. He recited:

"Well done he who has clothed me with a fur coat, which shall be my protection from shivering.

He has clothed me with it, preserving my heart's blood ... may he be preserved from the harm of men and Jinn!

Today he shall deck himself with my praise, tomorrow he shall be decked with the silk of Paradise!"

Now, when he had fascinated the company with his excellence, they threw to him furred robes and silken padded coats, as if the weight of them were too much to bear, and he could scarcely lift them and carry them himself. I followed him, and said "That was a sharp wind indeed which froze you, but do not go naked again like that." He replied "Fie on you! Swiftness to blame does not belong to the just; do not hasten to censure, for it is wrong; do not prosecute when you have no knowledge of the case. For by Him who has given the light of hoariness, and made the tomb of Medina sweet, had I not stripped myself I should have gone home a failure, to an empty wardrobe! But," and here he frowned, "do you not know that it is my nature to pass from prey to prey, yet you check me, and resist me. You make me lose double of what you have profited me; then spare me (God save you) from your vain talk, shut on me the door of your earnestness and jest."

But I pulled him with the string of playfulness and said: "By Allah, had I not kept your secret, and revealed you to the crowd, you would not have got one

gift! You would not have come away more coated than
an onion. So now recompense me for my goodness,
and for the covering I gave you, either by returning to
me my fur coat or by giving me some advice about
how to keep warm in winter." He looked at me very
angrily and said "As for returning your fur coat, that is
as impossible as restoring the yesterday that is past, or
the dead man that is gone. But I will give you this
which will help you:

'Winter comes and its needs to me are seven, when
the rain confines me from business:

A home, a purse, a stove, a cup of wine after the
roast meat, a pleasant wife, and clothing.'

"My dear friend, surely an answer like that is better
than a cloak that warms, so be content with what you
have learned and depart." So I parted from him, and
my fur coat's departure left me shivering all the rest of
the winter.

THE ENCOUNTER OF THE ADDRESS

Once I was in the city of Ahwaz in a state of great poverty, and so not being able to get hold of any money there, decided to seek my fortune elsewhere.

When I had come away from it for the space of two days and two nights, I met with a pitched tent and a glowing fire in the wilderness. I was delighted to see signs of some human individuals, so I went eagerly forward thinking "I will be able at least to warm myself here and maybe quench my thirst."

When I came closer, I saw some good-looking boy-servants, and valuable furniture, and there was sitting an old man in truly wondrous apparel, with fresh fruit in a bowl beside him. I greeted him and drew back, not wishing to intrude upon his thinking, but he pulled me towards him, and said "Will you not take this seat beside me, and enjoy the company of one whose fruit is choice, whose pleasantry charms?"

I took my seat there, to get the choice of what he would be likely to say, not to swallow down what was offered as food. Then as soon as he had unveiled his accomplishments and bared his teeth I knew that he was Abu Zayd by the beauty of his sayings and by the ugliness of those yellow teeth. And we knew each other then, and two joys encompassed me in that hour. I did not know which joy pleased me most, whether it was for the dawning of the darkness of his journeys, or at the plenitude of his dwelling after his poverty. So I said to him: "Where is your returning, and where is your going onward, and how has your wardrobe been filled?"

He replied "My coming is from Tus, and as for my destination, it is Sus; and as for the wealth which I have now, it is from an Address which I had composed." I begged him to tell me about the Address, and to recite it to me then. He said "The war of Al Basus was less a thing than what you would desire indeed, unless you accompany me to Sus."

So I attached myself to him, and was able to enjoy his company for about a month. He slaked my thirst to the full with the cups of his beguiling, and made me bear the bridle of my expectation. Until one day my patience was at an end, and I cried "There remains to you no pretext by which you can divert me further, for tomorrow I shall take omen of the raven of separation and leave you!"

He said "God forbid that I should break promise with you or thwart you! I will tell you the story which I have so long delayed to unfold. Add it to your 'Tales of Pleasure after Pain.' " I said "How long is your tether, how various are your wiles!" He said "Understand that frowning Time has cast me in these roles. I was swept by Fortune to Tus, poor and woe-laden. I had not even the kernel of a date-stone to eat. So the bareness of my hands made me resort to haltering myself with debt, and I took credit by evil chance from one who was hard of nature. I fancied that it would be easy to find a market for my poetry, and I spent a great deal; suddenly debt overwhelmed me, and the claimant for repayment beset me. I was utterly bewildered, and told him my difficulties, but he did not believe me when I pleaded poverty, and continued worrying me. Every time I humbled myself to him, and begged him to be generous, he refused, and would show me no mercy. He said to me "Do not set your heart on being waited for while you hold onto the bright gold which I have lent you; you will not see the path of deliverance unless you show me the melting of the pure ore."

I lost my temper then, and assaulted him, so that he would take me before the Governor of that place.

That was because I had heard much of the eminence of the Governor and the severity of the Kadi and his meanness. Now, when we were at the gate of the ruler of Tus, I knew that I should have neither hurt nor harm from him. I called for ink-flask and paper, and composed for him an excellent Address, and this is it:

"The qualities of our Lord are loved, and at his courtyard there is abiding; and nearness to him is as gifts, and farness from him is as destruction. His friendship is as pedigree, and his estrangement is as calamity; his sword's edge is sharp, and the stars of his virtue gleam. His continence adorns, and the rectitude of his road is plain. His understanding turns and tries, and his fame goes East and West. The Ruler, the intelligent, surpassing, excelling; understanding, ingenious; impatient of baseness, loathing it. Replacing, consuming; distinguished, incomparable, illustrious, virtuous, quick-witted, fastidious; marvellous when he discourses, able when the stir of ill befalls, and the dreaded calamity grows mighty. The chaplets of his honour are self-strung, and the rain-storm of his largess showers. The gift of his hand flows freely, and avarice from his heart sinks away. The teat of his liberality is milked, and the gold of his chests is spoiled. He whom his band gathers to itself prospers and overcomes; the merchant of his gate makes gain by beguiling him. He refrains from wronging the innocent, and is free from the foulness of the transgressor. He unites his gentleness with dignity, and turns aside from the path of the niggardly. He is not given to leap at the opportunity of evil, but abstains with the abstaining of the righteous. Therefore he is loved, and his continence merits the infatuation he inspires, since its pure essence beguiles all. His qualities are bright, and gleam; and his arrow is an arrow which overcomes when you shoot against it. He is gentle, he is cheerful, one who makes good when his friend slips, nor is there any doubt of his desert. Not miserly, no, but bountiful; open when he is solicited, one who goes forth, his gate does not keep him confined. When want bites, he breaks the edge of its biting by his succour, and its tooth falls out. And it is fitting that whoever is wise and understanding, whoever is near and far, should submit himself to the hero of the time, the restorer of the palsied. For since he sucked the breast of his fostering, he has been distinguished by the abundance of his shower. He raises the fallen, and comforts him; if he helps, he gladdens; if he contends in honour, he routs his enemy, and returns with a clear right. He prepares fatigue for him who shall rule after him; for that one shall have to work hard to imitate him — he is lauded as often as men move him to kindness, or prove him in deed; he crowns his virtues with the love of his suppliants. May he never become void of gladness, may the shadow of his prosperity be lengthened, for he is virtuous in the sight of whoever contemplates the shining of his stars. He adorns the graces of his culture by clothing himself with the fear of his Lord. May my Lord's prospering and gain of honours — firmly rooted and large — and may all his excelling be published, as they publish themselves. And may the helping of his servant with a portion of his abundance accord with the pious offerings of His Honour, for his servant is a child of the noble (though a wanderer from need), one wounded by calamities that have scarred him. His draught is but a draining, his food is borrowed, his dawn is his evening, and his cloak worn out. Now he quakes at the demands of a tyrannical debtor, who harasses him because of a debt that attaches to him like a leech. But if my Lord will mercifully avert him from me by the gifts of his hand, he will belt himself with the glory that surpasses, and come off with the reward of loosing me from the chain. May the qualities of his disposition never fail to aid whoever watches the promise of rain of his lightning-cloud. By the grace of the Lord, who is without beginning, who lives now, and is without end."

"The Governor, hearing the pearls of my Address, made a sign at once for the paying of the debt which plagued me, then he congratulated me, appropriated me for his ostension, and by his preference distinguished me. I remained a few years prospering in guestship with him, and pasturing in the oasis of his bounty. Until, when his gifts overwhelmed me, and his gold had lengthened my skirt, I contrived to depart in the fair condition in which you see me now."

Then I said to Abu Zayd "Thanks to Him that destined to you the meeting with the kind one!" He said "Praise be to God for the happiness of fortune and freedom from the contentious adversary! But, see now, what is it that would please you most − that I should share with you the gifts, or present you with the priceless Address?"

I said "The dictation of the Address would be more pleasing to me." He said "That, too, by the Truth, is lighter upon me; for truly the gift of that which goes in at the ears is much easier than the gift of that which comes out of the sleeve!" But then, as if he scorned his meanness, and grew ashamed, he gave me the Address and a fine present together. Thus I gained from him two lots, and parted from him with two booties, and returned to my home, cool of eye, for I had no cause to shed the hot tears of grief.

THE ENCOUNTER OF THE TENT-DWELLERS

In my early days, I had always wanted to join the people of the hair-tents, the Bedouin, and learn their ways, their language and their peace, so that I might take after their high-mettled spirits.

So I bestirred myself with the alertness of one not lacking in industry, and began to roam through lowlands and highlands, until I got together a string of camels and a flock of goats. Then I took myself to some Arabs far away from the towns, fit to be the lieutenants of kings. No care lighted upon me when I was with them, no arrow struck, until one night there strayed away one of my she-camels, profuse of milk flow. So I sprang upon a swift-paced steed, and fared forth. All night, in the full moon's light, I scoured the desert, every copse and treeless place, until the morning call to prayer came to my heart's ear. Then I got from my saddle, and said my prayers, after which I rode again, trying my poor mount to his utmost. While I was riding along, I saw no trace but I tracked it, saw no valley but I crossed it, met no rider but I questioned him, and in this way I covered many miles.

But my toil was useless, and I realized that the day being so hot, I had better rest somewhere, or find a shelter soon, or both I and my horse would succumb to the heat.

I rode towards a Sarhah tree, with its large branches, with boughs thickly leaved, that I might sleep in the shade till sundown. But before I had set my foot upon the earth, and caught my breath, I spied someone coming towards me, in the dusty clothes of a wayfarer. I rather grudged him a share of my shade, and was beginning to feel somewhat alarmed as to who it might be. My surprise was great when I discovered it to be none other than Abu Zayd of Seruj. He greeted me with friendship, and made me forget my loss, and I enquired of him what he was doing there and how he fared within and without.

With no further ado he began to tell me: "Say to him that would enquire into the inward state of my affairs, you will meet at my hands all honour and regard, as I am roving from land to land, a night traveller from one trackless desert to another. The chase yields me food, the sandal is my riding-beast, all my equipment the wallet and the ferruled staff. If I chance to alight in a city, my abode is the garret of the hostelry, and my boon-companion a scroll. There is nothing mine that I will miss when it is gone, or fret about when the wiles and vicissitudes of time rob me of them; save that I pass my nights free from concern, and my mind has severed partnership with sorrow. I sleep at night the fill of my eyelids, and my heart is cool of burning grief and anxiety. I reck not from what cup I sip, and sip again, or what is the sweetness that comes from the bitter-sweet. I do not allow abasement to become an easy road to bounties; for if an object of desire dons the raiment of shame, alas for him who courts a gift; and whenever a wretch inclines to baseness, my nature shrinks from his fashion."

I then told him the tale of my strayed camel, and what I had endured that day and the bygone night, and he said "Leave concerning yourself about departed things, or pine for that which has perished. Do not regret what is gone, even if it be a river of gold! Do not incline to him who veers from you, and kindles the fire of your anguish, though he were the son of your loins, or the brother of your soul." Then he added "Have you a mind to have your noonday nap now, and abstain from talk? For surely our bodies are jaded, and there is nothing to refurbish the mind and to enliven the languid like sleep at noon when the heat is fiercest; especially so in the last two months, when the skin of the camel shrivels through excessive thirst."

I replied "As you will, I have no wish to thwart you." Thereupon he made the ground his bed, and fell dozing, then apparently fell fast asleep. I sat for quite a while, leaning on my elbow, to keep watch, not succumbing to slumber; however, drowsiness overtook me, and I did not recover myself until night had crept in, and the stars were twinkling overhead. I soon found that there was no friend of Seruj, and no horse, and spent a night battling against my sullenness. I wondered if I ought to set off on foot, and in which direction I should wend my homeward way, when, at the smile of dawn, there appeared on the horizon a camel-rider, making his way over the plain with the speed of an ostrich. I signalled to him with my waving cloak, hoping to get him to turn in my direction. He did not heed me, unfortunately, nor did he take any notice of my anxiety, and I set off running towards him with tremendous haste and, getting near him, began to call out that I would like to mount up behind him, if he would take pity. But when I made upon him, by dint of hard running, I saw his mount was none other than my own lost camel. I dragged at the halter, and brought the beast to a stop, yelling at the rider every abuse I could think of, saying "I am her master! She and her colt and her milk are mine, she is the very one who has strayed from me". But he took to abusing me in return, and shouted, and would not be abashed, now cowering, now acting the lion. There came upon us Abu Zayd as if from nowhere. I called to him and asked if he were here to atone for yesterday's misdeeds, or to make good my wrong, or to encompass my utter ruin. He said "God forbid that I should despatch one whom I have wounded, or follow up my Simoon with a deadly night blast! Rather have I come to find out the truth of your state and condition, and to be a right hand to your left."

My anxiety was then allayed, my suspicions subsided. Then he took his lance and pointed it at the thief of my milch camel, saying to him with the glance of the lion in the thicket looking at its prey "I swear by Him who kindles the morning that if you do not make away with the swiftness of the fly, and content yourself with escape from death as the best of your booty, I will pierce your neck-vein and make your offspring and friends mourn for you!"

The fellow let go the halter of the camel and started to run off as if Satan were after him.

Abu Zayd said to me "Mount her hump and away with you. My brother, you who bear up with my injury better than my brethren and kinsfolk, if my yesterday has harmed you, my today has brought you joy, so forgive me because of this and spare me both thanks and blame."

I was at a loss, whether to rebuke him, or to try to balance the benefit I had received from him, but he turned his horse's head (my horse's head!) into the wind, and riding at a magnificent canter, was soon gone.

So I took seat on my beast, and hurried homeward, and after hap and mishap reached my tent-village at last.

THE TWENTY-EIGHTH ASSEMBLY

THE ENCOUNTER AT SAMARCAND

In one of my journeys I chose sugar-candy for a merchandise, making Samarcand my destination. In those days I was brimful of spirits, upright of build, taking sight from the bow of enjoyment at the target of pleasure, and seeking in the sap of my youth the glamours of the water-semblance, the mirages of life. Now, I reached Samarcand on a Friday morning, after much hardship, and spent the shortest possible time about my business, then went to wash for the prayer. I hastened humbly to the congregation which was forming itself and happily got a place quite near to where the preacher was going to stand. People were coming in twos and threes, till the mosque was very crowded, and I was glad that I was so near to the front. The preacher mounted the steps of the pulpit, and after waving his right hand in blessing began "Praise be to Allah, the exalter of names, the praised for His bounties, the abundant in gifts, the called-on for the rescinding of calamity, restorer of bones, king of the nations, honourer of the people of forbearance and generosity; Whose cognizance comes up with every secret, Whose compassion encompasses every obdurate in sin, Whose munificence comprises all the world, Whose power breaks down every revolter. I praise Him with the praise of one who proclaims God's Unity and professes Islam. I pray to Him with the prayer of the hopeful, the trusting, for He is the God, there is no God but He, the Unique, the One, the Just, the Eternal, there is none begotten to Him and no begetter, no companion with Him, and no helpmeet. He sent forth Mohammed to spread Islam, to consolidate religion, to confirm the guidance of the apostles, to straighten the backs of the black-hued and the red. He united womb-connections, taught the fundamentals of truth, set a stamp on the lawful and the forbidden, he laid down the rules for the doffing and the donning of the pilgrim robe. May Allah exalt his place and perfect the blessing and the benediction on him, may He have compassion on his race, the worthy, and on his progeny, as long as the clouds pour, as long as the dove coos, as long as the cattle graze, as long as the sword assaults. Work, and may Allah have mercy on you, the pious; exert yourselves towards your return, on the resurrection day, with the exertion of the sound, curb your lusts with the curbing of enemies, make ready for your departure with the readiness of the prepared. Portray to yourselves the imaginings of vicissitudes of fortune, attacks of sickness, and the cutting off from pelf and kin. Think of death, the agony of its throwing place, of the tomb and of the awfulness of that which is seen there, and of the loneliness of the one deposited in the grave-niche, of the angel and the frightfulness of his questioning and of his advent. Look at fortune and at the baseness of its onslaught, and of its deceit and its cunning. How many road-marks has it obliterated, and how many a host has it shattered, how many an honoured king has it overthrown. Its striving is to make deaf the ears, to make flow the tear-fronts, to baffle desires, to destroy the songster and the listener to the song. Its decree is the same for kings and subjects, for the lord and the henchman, for the envied and the envier, for the serpent and the lion. It turns away, and reverses hopes; it outrages and gives nothing but outrage; it does not gladden, but saddens, reviles and injures. It grants no health, but engenders disease and frightens friends. Fear Allah! Fear Allah! May Allah keep you! How long this persistency in levity, this perseverance in thoughtlessness, this stubbornness in sin, this loading yourselves with crime, this rejection of the word of the wise, this rebellion against the God of Heaven? Is not senility your harvest, and the clod of earth your couch? Is not death your capturer and the bridge Sirat (as thin as a hair and as sharp as a sword, over the fire of Hell) your path? Is not the hour of resurrection your tryst, and the plain of hell your goal? Are not the terrors of doomsday laid in ambush for you? Is not the abode of transgressors Al Hutamah, the Crushing? Their food, poison, their breathing-air the scorching blast? No wealth prospers them, no offspring, no numbers protect them. But lo, Allah has mercy upon the man who rules his passion, and who treads the path of his Guidance; who makes firm his obedience; and strives for the restfulness of his place of refuge; who works while life lasts, with fortune at truce with him, and health and perfect welfare at hand. May Allah inspire you with the alighting of afflictions, may He reward you with the robe of inspiration, may you be caused to live in the abode of peace, of Him I ask that you be shown mercy, for He is the most forgiving, the most generous, the saviour; may peace be with you!"

Now, when I saw what a choice thing without a flaw that sermon was, like a bride without a spot, the wonder at it made me look closely at the preacher, and as I scanned his face, I began to be aware that this was Abu Zayd once more. After the people began to disperse, I ran towards him, and found him coming quickly towards me, to do me honour, and he bade me accompany him to his house. He said that after a meal he would make me the confidant of his intimate affairs. When the wing of night had spread, and it was the time for sleep, he brought forth some wine-flasks. I said to him "Do you drink before sleep, and you a prayer-leader of the people?" "Hush," he answered, "By day I am a preacher and by night I make merry."

I said "By Allah, I do not know whether to wonder more at your unconcern for your kinsfolk and your birthplace, or at your preacher-office with your foul rotation of your winecup!"

He answered "Listen to me: weep not for a friend that is distant, nor for an abode, but turn yourself about as fortune turns you around; fancy all the earth your home, and all mankind your dwelling-place. Forbear with the ways of him with whom you are dealing, and humour him, for the wise humour.

"Do not miss any day of enjoyment, for you do not know if you will live a day or an age. Know that death is going around, and the moon-haloes circle above all created beings, swearing that they will not cease chasing them, as long as morn and evening turn and return. How then can you ever expect to escape from the net?"

Then when the wine cups went between us from hand to hand, and the vital spirits waxed gleeful, he extracted from me an oath to guard his secret. So I complied with his wish, and kept faith with him, and let down the skirt before the turpitudes of the night.

THE TWENTY-NINTH ASSEMBLY

THE ENCOUNTER AT WASIT

The decree of declining fortune driving me to Wasit, I took lodging for the night at a khan, which housed a wild medley of travellers, human jumble from every land. It was a clean enough place, with not an excessive rent, and with the civility of its inhabitants enticed the stranger to make his home, even for a short time, among them. I was secluded in one of the quiet chambers, when I heard my next-door neighbour say to his fellow-dweller in the room, "Rise up, my dear son, may your luck not be set, nor your adversary be on your track — take the one of the full-moon face and the pearly hue, who was pinched and stretched, imprisoned and released, made to drink and weaned, and pushed into the fire after he had been slapped. Then career to the market the career of the longing swain, and bring back instead of it the pregnant that impregnates, the spoiler who enriches, the saddener who gladdens, the possessor of a puff that sets on fire, and of a germ that breaks forth in light, of an utterance that satisfies, and of a gift that profits, who, when he is struck thunders and lightens, and reveals himself in flames, and who sputters on tinder rags."

Then as soon as the noise of the throat-bag of the camel had subsided, there was nothing left but the going of him who had to go, and there sallied forth a graceful youth with a graceful swagger. So I set out in the wake of the youth to try and make sense of the riddle I had heard.

Searching among the row of market shops, the

youth came to a store of flint-stones and gave their seller a loaf, receiving a flint from him in return. Then I wondered at the sagacity of the sender and the sent one, and I knew that it was of Seruji growth, and I hurried back to the khan, to test the truth of my surmise, and to see if my arrow had reached the mark.

I proved myself to be an expert in sharpness of understanding, as well as hearing, for Abu Zayd was sitting in the courtyard of the khan.

Then we congratulated each other on the meeting, and mutually paid the dues of welcoming friends. He asked me "What happened to you, that you should have quitted your place?" and I answered "Fortune broke and oppression was rife."

He replied "By Him that sends down the rain, and makes the fruit come forth from its sheath, times are foul and wrong prevails, and the helper is not to be found. How did you get away and when did you leave?" "I made night my shirt and escaped, a starveling," I told him.

Then he made some holes in the ground with his stick, and thought how he could find a loan somewhere to benefit me. Presently he said, with the stirring of one to whom a prey is near, "It just occurred to my heart that you might ally yourself with one who would heal your wound and feather your wing."

"Who will have me, Nobody, son of Nobody that I am?" I said shortly, for I knew that he was going to embark upon one of his schemes.

"I will help you," he said, "I will drop hints about you, about your pedigree, your kith and kin of high renown, and so forth. Some pleasant family will be delighted to welcome such as you into their bosom, and I guarantee it will not be long before you are wed to a most suitable one."

My spirits were roused, and even more so when he continued "I will deliver at the place of your betrothal and at the gathering of your wedding guests an address such as has never entered any ear, and has not been pronounced at any assembly."

I said to him "Then I will entrust you with the arrangements," and he rose, trotting away briskly with his usual stride, and returned beaming very soon. "Rejoice at the tidings of fortune and the milking of an abundant flow," he said. "I have already been charged with fixing the marriage contract by the happy father, and stood security for the money, so the thing is all but settled." He rose and told all the people of the khan about the coming nuptials, and arranged about the sweetmeats for the table. Then when night had extended her tent ropes, he called out to the assembly "Come, be present at once," and all came immediately to enter his room. Now, when they stood in rows before him, and witness and witnessed were gathered, he busied himself in raising the astrolabe and lowering it, and in consulting the almanack and laying it aside, until the people became drowsy and sleep drew near.

I said to him "O Sir, put the axe to the block, and free the people from sleepiness!"

Then he cast a glance at the stars, and breaking loose from the tie of silence, he swore by Mount Tur, and the written Book, that the secret of this hidden matter should be unravelled, and its memory spread forth to the Day of Judgement. Then he sat in a kneeling position, and invited the people to feed on his address, saying "Praise be to Allah, the Fashioner of every born one, the refuge of every outcast, the spreader of the earth's couch, the fastener of the mountains, the sender of rains, the smoother of difficulties, who knows all secrets and penetrates them, who overthrows kings and destroys them, who makes the ages follow each other, who initiates affairs and brings them to an issue. His bounty is universal and perfect, His rainclouds pour and shower, He answers requests and hopes, he makes it easy for the distressed, I praise Him with the praise that endures through all time. I proclaim His unity, as Abraham, the Sorrowful, proclaimed it, for there is no God but He, He sent Mohammed to take the Message, may Allah never cease to bestow honour on him, and his family, and bring his spirit to the abode of peace, as long as the mirage glitters, as the young ostrich runs, as a new moon rises, as a shout that greets the same is heard. Then work, you who tread the path of lawfulness, throw off the forbidden, listen to the command of Allah, and obey it, unite the blood-relations and revere them, resist lusts and repel them. Cut yourselves off from wantonness and greed, ally yourselves with the people of piety and righteousness. Now, the seeker of your alliance is the purest of freemen as to birth, and the noblest of them as to lordliness, the sweetest as for a watering-place, and the soundest for keeping his word. He has come to you for a bride and to settle a dowry upon her, and he is the worthiest of sons-in-law. He who gives in marriage to him does not err, and the one who enters into relationship with him is not foiled nor soiled. I ask from Allah for you to approve of his connection, and to prosper him lastingly, and may He inspire each one to seek improvement of his state and to make ready for his return. God is Great! To Him Eternal praise and glory to His Messenger Mohammed!"

Now, when he had ended his address, he concluded the marriage contract at the settlement of five hundred dinars, after which he said to me "For ease and sons!" Then he brought forth the sweetmeats which he had prepared, and when I was stretching out my hand for one he stopped me from eating, urging me to pass them round before I served myself.

By Allah, it was not long before the people began to get very drowsy indeed, and their chins fell onto their chests, deep in sleep. Then when I saw them as though thrown down by the daughter of the winecask, I knew that this was the very mother of mischiefs, so I said to him "O you arch-fiend! What have you prepared for the guests, poisoned sweets?" Said he "They will soon wake, I just prepared a mess of *banj* (hashish) in trays of the khalanj tree."

Then I said "I swear by Him who makes the stars rise in brightness and guides by them all wayfarers, you have done a shameful thing and secured yourself a record among shameful deeds!"

I was bewildered as to what would become of me at the discovery of this trick; my soul fluttered within me distractedly, and my side-muscles quivered with fright. Abu Zayd saw the extent of my fear and said "What is this burning thought and this white-fear? If your concern at my offence is for the sake of me, know that I am now well off and shall soon be quite out of sight and ken of these people. But if it is with a view to yourself, and from apprehension of your imprisonment, then partake of one of the sweets which they have left, and be found in the same state, for I will rob you of your shirt to look as if you have suffered with the rest! But if not, then fly before your share of this be discovered."

Before my astonished gaze he began to clear the room of anything of value, belonging to the wedding guests, which he could carry off with him. Then after he had done the loot up in bundles which he could carry, tucked up his sleeves and girded himself for flight, he said in the voice of one who is a sincere friend "Have you a mind to go with me to the Batihah, so that I could unite you with yet another fair one?"

Then I said that by Him who had created me, it was not my habit to marry one bride after another in khans, and as he stepped forward to embrace me in farewell I stepped aside to avoid him.

Seeing my repugnance, he said sadly: "O you, who turn away from me, and rebuke me for my foul treatment of those I had for neighbours, you do not comprehend what I have done, but I know them all full well; I sought their hospitality and I saw them unheedful of their guests; I probed them, and when I tested them I found them to be base coin. Among them is none who does not strike terror when he can, or else is terror-stricken; there is none sincere in friendship, none trustworthy, none benevolent, none kindly disposed.

"So I sprang upon them with the spring of the tearing wolf upon the sheep, and left them prostrate, as if they had been made to drink the cup of death. And my hand possessed itself of what they had hoarded; how much have I gained by my cunning that was not ordained by the sword, and stood my ground in terrors, such as lions would shrink from facing. How often have I shed blood, slain unawares and desecrated the sanctuary of the high-minded! How many a pernicious rush have I taken into sin! But withal I have laid in a goodly opinion with regard to my Lord, the Compassionate."

Now when he had reached this couplet, he began to weep and asked for forgiveness, until he propitiated the inclination of my heart that had turned from him, and I hoped for him what is hoped for the guilty who confesses his guilt. Then he stopped his tears and putting his wallet under his armpit, made off, saying to his son: "Carry the rest, and Allah be your Protector." So when I saw the snake and the little snake glide away, I knew that my tarrying in the khan would plunge me into disgrace, so I quickly gathered my few chattels and gathering my skirt for flight, passed the night in faring towards Tib, relying on Allah to protect me from the mischief of the preacher.

THE THIRTIETH ASSEMBLY

THE ENCOUNTER AT SUR

I fared from the City of Mansur, Baghdad, to the town of Sur (Tyre), and when I had become there the possessor of high rank and of the power to raise and abase, I longed for Cairo and, setting off speedily like an ostrich, left behind me all my impediments.

Now, when I had entered her, I was once more delighted with all her beauties, and dazzled by the break of morning brightness there.

When I was one day loitering about, upon a steed of stately pace, I beheld, on short-haired nags, a group of men dressed as gloriously as the lamps of night. I asked how I could join such a troop, and where they might be going, and was told that they were a wedding-party. Then the sprightliness of youth urged me along with them, and I expected that I would get a fair share of the bridal sweets and a meal at the wedding feast. Presently we came, after enduring a long ride, to a huge mansion, wide and high, which testified to the builder's wealth and station in life.

When we alighted from horseback and entered the courtyard I saw its vestibules adorned with old tattered garments, and garlanded with begging-baskets, which surprised me somewhat. There was an aged man sitting on a pile of gorgeous stuffs, upon a handsome bench. I asked him who was the owner of this mansion and why it was so decorated with these rags, as it was supposed to be a wedding feast. Said he, "It has no distinct owner and no manifest master, it is the inn of importunate beggars and low artisans, and the den of ballad-singers and blind rehearsers of the Traditions."

Then I said to myself, "What an idiot I am to have come upon this fool's errand" and intended to return at once, but then I felt it would appear churlish if I did so. So I entered the house reluctantly, as one drinking draughts that make one choke, or as the sparrow which enters the cage. Then lo, there were inside the most richly adorned state chairs, carpets spread everywhere, fine silken cushions laid in rows, and beautiful curtains. Presently the bridegroom swaggered forth, arrayed in his clothes of richest striped stuff, and when he sat down someone on the side of his relatives called out: "By the reverence due to Sasan, grand master of masters, and pattern of sturdy beggars, none ties the knot this day but he who has roamed and roved, who has been young and waxed old in adversity." Then the company on the bride's side were well pleased with the groom's people with regard to bringing in such a splendid one as they had mentioned. In came an old man whose stature the days and nights had bent, and they rose to welcome him. When he and they were seated, and the turmoil of voices had subsided, he advanced to his cushion, and stroked his hoary beard with his hand, and spoke:

"Praise be to Allah, the foremost in munificence, the ever new in bestowing bounties, to Whom we are brought near by supplication, on Whom we are made to rely for the accomplishment of hopes, Who has sternly ordained the legal alms from every property and commanded to feed him that begs and him that refuses to beg; Who has described His servants in the Book: 'Those who know well that the suppliant and the destitute have a claim on their riches'; I praise Him for what He has dispensed of wholesome food, and I take refuge in Him from hearing a prayer void of intention. I testify that there is no God but He, the One, who requites the alms-giving men and women and rewards alms with lavish interest. Furthermore, I attest that He sent Mohammed as His sincere servant, that he might efface the darkness by light, and secure for the poor a share from the rich, may God bless him and hallow him. Allah has made matrimony a law so that you may be chaste, and instituted propagation that you may multiply, for so did He say 'O ye men, we have created you from a male and a female, and made you clans and tribes, so that you might recognize each other,' and this you all know.

"Now this is Abud-darraj Wallaj, son of Karraj, lord of the impudent face, and manifest mendacity, of yelping and shouting, of importunity and persistency in begging; who woos the shrew of her people, fit mate for her husband, Qanbas, daughter of Abu-Anbas, for the sake of that which reached him of her being clad with pertinacity, and her excessiveness of stooping to beggary, and her quickness in grasping a livelihood, and her rising after a fall, along with her combativeness. And he has lavished upon her for a dowry a wallet and a ferruled stick, together with a kerchief and a pitcher. So marry him as one like him is to be married, and join your rope with his rope, and if you fear poverty or want, through increase of family, Allah will give you a sufficiency out of His bounty. Thus I say my say, craving forgiveness from Allah, the Mighty, for me and you, and praying that He might multiply your offspring in the beggar-dens, and guard you from all dangers."

Then, when the Shaykh had ended his discourse, and pressed upon the bride's relatives her contract, there fell a scatter of coins that exceeded the limits of abundance, and would have made the miser to excel in liberality. Thereupon the Shaykh rose, trailing his skirts and preceding his rabble. I followed him, so that I might see the array of the people and complete the enjoyment of the day. He turned with them to a table that its dressers had adorned, and whose every side equalled the other in beauty. When each one had seated himself in his proper place, I slipped out of the

row, and fled from the throng. But then it happened
that a turn of the Shaykh's face made me look in his
direction, and a glance from his eyes caught me
unawares, and he said "Where are you going, you cur-
mudgeon? Do you not like the company of those who
are generous?"

I asked: "By Him who created the heavens one after
another, what was the sprawling-place of your youth,
where is your breeze blowing?" He said "My birthplace was Seruj, a city that is filled to overflowing;
her waters spring from Salsabil, her fields are pleasure-
meads, her sons and her palaces are stars and sidereal
mansions. O the flowers of her hills when the snows
have melted away, who sees her says the haven of
earthly Eden is Seruj. To him who leaves her are sighs
meted and smothered weeping, such as I have met
since the Barbarians drove me out, tears that pour
bitterly in anguish, that scarcely calmed, will rage
afresh, day-long griefs that distract the mind. Would
that my fatal day had come, when I was fated to depart
from her."

I knew for certainty that it was none other than my
old friend Abu Zayd, though old age had now shackled
him. So I put my hand in his, and I reckoned it a boon
to eat with him from his platters. I continued during
my stay in Cairo, going nightly to him, to sit by his
guest-fire, and fill both my shells with the pearls of his
utterance, till the raven of separation croaked to us and
I parted with him as reluctantly as the lid would part
with the eye.

THE THIRTY-FIRST ASSEMBLY

THE ENCOUNTER AT RAMLAH

In the freshness of my youth, I hated making my den in the towns, and loved slipping out of the scabbard, and knew that travel fills the travelling-bags and produces gain, so I shook the divining-arrows and started towards the shores of Sham for the purpose of trading.

Now, when I had tented at Ramlah, and had thrown down the staff of travel, I found there three caravans being made ready for a journey to the Mother of Cities, Mecca.

The gale of longing blew strongly within me, so that I haltered my camel, and threw from me all engagements and ties I had made previously. Then I strung myself together with travelling companions like the stars of heaven, who in their faring sped with the torrent's rush. So, between night-journeying and travelling by day, between trotting and ambling, we arrived at Juhfah, the station where the pilgrims from Syria assembled, before setting out for the general meeting-place, Muzdalifeh, next to Holy Mecca. We alighted, each from our own beast, making ready for donning the pilgrims's robe, wishing each other joy in arriving so near to our desire. But no sooner had we made our animals kneel in the place, and laid down the saddle-bags, than there came among us down from the mountains a person, bare of skin who cried plaintively "O young and old people of this concourse, listen to that which rescues on the day of the mutual call, when those who are in paradise shall call to those of the

Fire!" The pilgrims hastened to hear what it was that he had to say, and he ascended one of the earth-mounds, so that they might hear better.

"O you company of pilgrims, flocking together from the mountain-paths, do you comprehend what you are about to face and whom you go to meet? Or do you know whom you approach and what you are undertaking so boldly? Do you imagine that the Haj is the choosing of saddle-beasts, the traversing of stations, the taking of seats in litters, and the loading of beasts of burden? Do you opine that piety is the tucking up of sleeves, the emaciating of bodies, the separation from children and the getting far from your native place? No, by Allah, it is the shunning of transgression before preparing the beast, the sincerity of purpose for making for that building there, and the purity of submission along with the fervour of devotion, the mending of dealings, before working the doughty camels. By Him who prescribed the rites for the devout, and guides straight the wanderer in the raven-black night, washing from bucketfuls does not cleanse from being immersed in the mire of sin, and the stripping of bodies does not counterbalance being laden with crime. Nor does the donning of the pilgrim's cloak make amends for being wrapped up in the forbidden. The being plaided with the pilgrim linen profits not, when one is burdened with iniquities, nor avails the seeking of approach to God by getting one's head shaved when one busies oneself in shaving mankind. Obsequiousness in clipping the hair, after completion of the pilgrimage, does not rub off the dirt of persistency in shortcomings. None prospers by visiting Mount Arafat but he who is endowed with wisdom, nor is anyone blessed by Al Khayf, who is addicted to injustice. None witnesses the standing place of Abraham but he who stands straight and upright, and who does not swerve from the right path. So Allah have mercy on the man who is sincere, before his running to Mount Safa, and treads the road of the divine pleasure, before repairing to the tanks of the Well Zamzam. The Haj is not your travelling by day and night, your selecting camels and camel-litters, the Haj is that you go to the holy house for the sake of Haj, not that you should accomplish your wants that way. That you bestride the back of righteousness, taking the check of lust for guide, and truth for high-road; that you bestow what has been given you when it is in your power, to him who in his need tenders his hand towards your gift. A pilgrimage with all this fraught is perfect, but if the Haj is void it proves abortive. For a losing bargain of dissemblers it suffices that they plant and do not reap, having met with toil and exile, and that they go without reward or praise, giving their frame a bait to him that censures and lampoons. See then, dear brother, what sacrifice you may offer up in the face of God, the Guardian, the going in and out. For no hidden deed shall remain hidden from the Compassionate, whether the servant be sincere or shamming. Steal a march on death by good deeds sent before; death's sudden summons, when it comes, will not be put off; and use humility in frame of mind, such as the nights, in their turn, cannot alter, though they give you a crown. Do not watch every cloud which flashes lightning though it appears to pour a copious shower of rain; not every caller merits to be heard; how many a whisperer shouted fatal news, and none is wise but he who contents himself with a morsel, that makes life's days to fold by degrees. For every large portion comes to be a mite, and meek grows every stiff-necked one, rage as he may!"

Now when he had fructified the barrenness of our understanding with the witchcraft of his telling, I sniffed the breeze of Abu Zayd, and delight made me incline to him with a thrill of affection. But I kept still until he had completed his expounding, and came down from his hillock. I slipped towards him, so that I might scan the traits of his countenance and descry the nature of his accomplishments. And lo, it was the stray for whom I had searched long, the threader of the pearls that he had displayed. Then I clung to him with the clinging of affection, and ranked him as recovery is ranked with the sick, and I asked him to join me, but he refused, saying: "I have made oath on this my pilgrimage, that I will neither ride together nor alternately with anyone, neither make gain nor boast of pedigree, neither seek profit, nor companionship, nor accommodate myself to him who dissembles." Then he left me in haste, and left me wailing, while I tried to keep him in sight, till he had climbed away into one of the mountain paths which swallowed him. I remembered his parting words as I lost him yet once more, and they were these: "He who visits on the backs of beasts is not like he who comes on foot; send them forward, those deeds of acceptance, scorn the tinsel of this earthly life, for its existence is but nothing. Remind yourself of the arrow of Death, when unawares his stroke falls, and bewail your work of shame, shed tears of blood for it, curing it with sore repentance, before the hide is rotten all through. May it be then that Allah guard you, against the fire that blazes fiercely, on the day when sin is cancelled no more, and tardy repentance vain."

Afterwards, I did not cease to look for him, at every water-station we came to, and every night-camp where we pillowed, until I fancied that the Jinn had snatched him from me.

THE THIRTY-SECOND ASSEMBLY

THE ENCOUNTER AT TAYBEH

This is one of the most elaborate and important, as well as one of the longest and most difficult of the Assemblies. Harith has completed the ceremonies of the Pilgrimage to Mecca, and intends to follow it up by the visit to Mohammed's tomb at Taybeh, one of the names given to Medina. On his road he meets in the homestead of one of the intermediate Arab tribes Abu Zayd, who this time has assumed the character of a mufti or jurisconsult and adept in the sacred and secular law of Islam. A large gathering of people has collected around him, whose spokesman proposes to him a hundred questions on various canonical and legal points, such as the religious obligations of ceremonial ablution, prayer, fasting, with almsgiving, pilgrimage, on buying and selling, the duties of magistrates towards orphans or weakminded persons, on principles of moral conduct, and so on — questions which are calculated to exhibit Abu Zayd at the same time as learned in the law and in the rarest idioms of the Arabic tongue. For his answers, while startling the ordinary hearer by being the opposite of what would be expected, prove perfectly correct, if the leading word be taken in a certain more recondite sense. For instance the question is: "May a woman be rebuked for being bashful?" to which Abu Zayd, no doubt to Mrs. Grundy's horror, replies "To be sure," because he gives to the verbal noun *khajal,* in everyday parlance "being ashamed or bashful," the rarer meaning of "being overbearing when in possession of riches," in support of which Hariri quotes a remarkable saying of Mohammed, recorded in the Traditions. As Chenery appositely observes, similar puzzles were not unknown in Europe, such as the question: "Num peccatum est occidere patrem suum," where not "one's own father," but "the father of swine," is meant. Hariri has not given the interpretation of the ambiguous terms as an integral part of the text, but inserted it in parenthesis after each question, and with the help of these explanations, which, in case of need, we have supplemented with a few additional remarks, the reader will find no difficulty in following the general drift of the Assembly. If some of the questions appear childish, he must remember that Hariri, while satisfying to the fullest extent the taste of his countrymen for the discussion of grammatical, rhetorical, and religious points of controversy, raises himself with a fine touch of irony above it, where such discussions degenerate into mere quibbles. But for the most part, we feel confident the reader will be amused and interested, and as a study on the synonymous and idioms of the Arabic Language the Assembly is invaluable.

At one time when I had completed the rites of the Haj and absolved the duties of [the shout] *labbaika,* and the outpour of the blood of the sacrifice, I resolved to make for Taybeh, with a travelling company of the Benu Shaibah, to visit the tomb of the Prophet, the Elected, and to disengage myself from the tribe of those "who perform the Haj and neglect him (Mohammed)." Now it was rumoured that the roads were unsafe and the Arabs of the two sanctuaries at war. So I was bewildered between fear that made me lag, and longing that stirred me on, until submissiveness was infused into my heart, and the predominance of [my desire for] the visiting of him upon whom be peace. Therefore, after having chosen my beast, and made ready my travelling-gear, I journeyed along with my companions without inclining to any halt, or remissness in faring on day and night, till we came to the Benu Harb, who had just returned from the war. Then we made up our minds to pass the length of the day in the encampment of the people, and while we were selecting a place for making our camels kneel down, and spying for the watering-pond, and a cool drink, lo, we saw them running as if they were flocking to some idol. So their swarming roused our suspicions, and we asked what was the matter with them. Then we were told that a learned legist of the Arabs was present in their assembly, and that this was the reason of their turmoil. Said I to my company: "Let us witness the gathering of the clan, so as to learn clearly to distinguish the right from the wrong." Thereupon they said: "Truly, what you propose is worth hearing, and you have given good advice without stint." Accordingly we rose to follow our guide and repair to the assembly, until, when we came near it, and stretched our necks to see the legist to whom they had crowded, I found him to be Abu Zayd, the father of lies and tricks, and of mischief and choice rhymes. He had donned the turban in the orthodox fashion and gathered his garment in proper syle, and was sitting crosswise, while the great ones of the clan surrounded him, and their medley enwrapped him from all sides. Presently he said to them: "Put questions to me on the points of intricacy, and let me explain to you all difficulties, for by Him who created the heavens, and taught Adam the names [of all things], I am the legist of the Arabs of the Arabians, and the most learned of those that live under the star-pocked sky." Then there stalked up to him a man glib of tongue, stout of heart, saying: "Know that I have had converse with the legists of the world to the effect that I have selected from them a hundred decisions, and if thou be of those who loathe the daughters of others (meaning lies, untruth, falsehood), and desire from us sound food, then listen and answer, so that thou mayest get thee thy due." He replied: "God is greatest (Allah akbar), the truth will become evident, and the hidden be disclosed, so say what thou art bidden." He said: "What sayest thou with regard to him, who has made an ablution (*wuzu*), and afterwards touched the back of his shoe?" He replied: "His ablution is invalidated by his doing so" (*na'l*, a shoe, and also "wife"). He said: "And when he has made an ablution, and afterwards the cold has thrown him on his side?" He replied: "Then let him renew his ablution" (*al-bard*, cold, and also "sleep"). He said: "May one who makes an ablution rub with his hands his testicles?" He replied: "He is invited to do so, but it is not made obligatory on him" (*unsai*, the two testicles, and also "both ears"). He said: "Is it allowed to make ablution with that which the serpent emits?" He replied: "And is there anything cleaner than it for the Arabs?" (*su'ban*, a large serpent, and also pl. of *sa'b*, "water-course in a valley, river"). He said: "Is the water [fetched by the hands of] a blind man lawful?" He replied: "Yea, and let that of the seeing man be avoided" (*zarir,* the word translated by blind man, in which case the water fetched by him would not be lawful for ablution, because he cannot know whether it is pure or not, means also "river-side", against the water of which there is no objection. On the other hand *al-basir,* the seeing man, means also "dog", and in their case the reverse would hold good: the water fetched by the former is chosen with discernment, and therefore not to be avoided, while "the water of the dog" would be the height of abomination). He said: "Is washing (*ghusl*) incumbent upon him who has lost sperm?" He replied: "Nay, even if he does so a second time" (*amna,* he lost or emitted sperm, and also "he went to Mina," the sacred valley near Mecca). He said: "Is it then incumbent on one polluted by seminal loss to wash his fur-coat?" He replied: "To be sure, and also his needle" (*al-farwah,* fur-coat, means also "skin of the head," and *al-ibrah,* needle, has moreover the signification "bone of the elbow"). He said: "Is circumambulation in the spring permitted?" He replied: "This is abominated on account of the execrable occurrence" (*tatawwuf,* circumambulation, means also "easing nature," and *ar-rabi',* spring, early vegetation, signifies also "streamlet," the defilement of which would be a hideous crime). He said: "Is the washing of his book incumbent on him?" He replied: "Yea, and also of his lip" (*as-sahifah,* book, and also "lines of the face"). He said: "How is it then, if he fails to wash his hatchet?" He replied: "It is as though he neglected to wash his head" (*al-fa's,* hatchet, and also "bone of the occiput"). He said: "Is it allowed to wash in a wallet?" He replied: "It is like washing in wells" (*jirab,* a leather bag, and also "the inside of a well"). He said: "And what sayest thou with regard to one who has used sand for his ablution, and afterwards sees gardens?" He replied: "His rubbing with sand is void, and he has to make his ablution afresh" (*rauz,* pl. of *rauzah,* garden, and also "a small quantity of water remaining in a cistern"). He said: "Is it allowed that a man should make his prostration upon ordure?" He replied: "Yea, and let him avoid the dirty one" (*'azirah,* human excrement, and also "a courtyard"). He said: "Is it then permitted to make prostration upon [the wood of] a Khilaf [-tree]?" He replied: "Nay, nor either on the edges of his garments" (*khilaf,* and *safsaf* or poplar-tree, on which prostration is not forbidden, and also "sleeve," on which a man is not allowed to make his prostration, as little as on his *atraf,* in the sense of edges of a garment in the text, while if the word is taken in the meaning of "extremities of the body, hands, and feet," the prostration upon them is in accordance with the tradition: "I was commanded to prostrate myself on seven bones," namely, the two feet, the two knees, the two forearms, and the forehead). He said: "What then if he make prostration on his left?" He replied: "There is no harm in his doing so" (*shimal,* the left side, and also pl. of *shimlah,* "cloak enveloping the whole body"). He said: "Is it then allowed to make prostration on trotters?" He replied: "Yea, with exception of the forearms" (*al-kura',* here translated by trotters, means that part in cattle which corresponds to the pastern of a horse, which as part of a dead animal would be considered unclean, but at the same time the word means "a projecting piece of stony ground or rock," on which prostration might take place, unless it serves to ease the forearms). He said: "Is it allowed that one should pray upon a dog's head?" He replied: "Yea, as well as upon all other high places" (*ras al-kalb,* dog's head, is apart from its literal meaning the name of a well-known mountain-cliff). He said: "Is it lawful for a student to carry copies of the Koran?" He replied: "Nay, nor to carry them in wrappers" (*daris,* a student, and also "a menstruous woman"). He said:

"And what sayest thou with regard to him who prays while the hair of his pubes appears?" He replied: "His prayer is lawful" (*al-'anah,* hair round the pudenda, and also "herd of asses," in connection with which latter meaning the word *barizah* would have to be translated in its literal meaning of coming out or sallying forth). He said: "How then if he has said prayer while [the obligation of] a fast was on him?" He replied: "He must reiterate it, and if he has prayed a hundred days" (*saum,* fasting, and also "excrement dropped by an ostrich"). He said: "But if he has carried a puppy while praying?" He replied: "It is as if he had carried beans (*jirw,* the young of a dog, and also small cucumbers, pomegranates, or similar fruit). He said: "Is the prayer of one who carries a hernia with him sound?" He replied: "Nay, and if he had been praying on [the holy] mount Marwah" (*garwah,* a rupture, and also "the vessel from which a dog drinks"). He said: "How then if on the garment of one praying any bodily excretion has fallen?" He replied: "His prayer takes effect, and no doubt" (*najw* is a general term for anything coming out of the belly, and therefore considered ceremonially impure, but it means also "a pouring cloud," the drops of which fallen on a man would not invalidate his prayer). He said: "Is it allowed that one covered with a woman's veil should lead a man in prayer?" He replied: "Yea, and also one in armour may lead him" (*muqunna',* one who wears the female veil *miqna',* implying that women are unfit to be Imams, and also "covered with a helmet"). He said: "But what if one has led them in whose hand there is an object of a pious donation?" He replied: "They will have to begin afresh, and if they were a thousand" (*waqf,* any object consecrated to pious purposes, and also "a bracelet of ivory or tortoiseshell," in the latter sense indicating that a wearer of such, *i.e.,* a woman, is excluded from the Imamship). He said: "What then if one has led them whose thigh is visible?" He replied: "His prayer and theirs is efficacious" (*fakhizuhu badiyah* [a man] whose thigh is bare, and also "whose tribal division or kindred are desert Arabs." Hariri remarks that some lexicographers prefer in the latter meaning the reading *fakhz*, instead of *fakhiz*, for the sake of distinction). He said: "But if the hornless bullock has led them?" He replied: "Say thy prayer, and no woe betide thee" (*as-saur al-ajamm*, a bullock without horns, and also "a lord or prince without a spear"). He said: "Can the prayer of the witness be curtailed or shortened?" He replied: "Nay, by the Invisible, the All-seeing" (*salat-ash-shahid*, the prayer of the witness, here meaning especially the blood-witness or martyr in religious warfare, and also "the prayer of sunset," so called because it coincides with the rising of the stars, to which the name *shahid* is given). He said: "Is it allowed for the excused to break fast in the month of Ramadan?" He replied: "It is not permitted except to little children" (*ma'zur*, or *mu'azzar*, excused, and also "circumcised"). He said: "Is it then open to one who brings home his bride to eat therein?" He replied: "Yea, to the fill of his mouth" (*al-mu'arris*, one bringing home a bride, and also "a traveller who takes a short rest at the end of night and presently continues his journey"). He said: "But what if therein the naked break their fast?" He replied: "The authorities gainsay them not" (*al-'urat*, pl. of *'ari*, the naked, and also irr. pl. of *muarrawin*, "seized by an ague," *'urawa'*). He said: "And if the faster eat on entering the morning?" He replied: "This is the more circumspect and safer for him" (*asbah*, he has entered on the morning, and also "he has lighted a lamp, *misbah*"). He said: "What then if he venture on eating at night?" He replied: "Let him be prepared to receive judgment" (*lail-an*, adverbial accusative, at night, and also acc. of *lail*, meaning according to Ibn Dorayd "the young of a bustard," and according to others "that of the partridge or the crane"). He said: "And how when he eats before the fair one has withdrawn from sight?" He replied: "Judgment, by Allah [the punishment of the law], is due on him" (al-baiza, woman, wife, and also "sun"). He said: "But if the faster provokes vomiting (by taking an emetic)?" He replied: "He has broken his fast, by Him who has made the chase lawful" (al-kaid, violent anger, and also "vomiting," to produce which the breaking of the fast is permitted, while the provoking of anger has nothing to do with it). He said: "Is it open to him to break the fast if the cook clings to him?" He replied: "Yea, but not the cook who dresses the food in the kitchen" (tabikh, cook, and also "a hot fever"). He said: "What then if a woman have laughed during her fast?" He replied: "The fasting of that day is invalidated for her" (zahikat, she laughed, and also "she became menstruous," as in Koran, xi. 74: "and she became menstruous and we announced Isaac to her"). He said: "But if smallpox appears on her fellow-wife?" He replied: "Let her break the fast, if she has made known her ailment" (zarrah, a fellow or rival wife, whose sickness would not dispense the former from fasting, and also "the root of the thumb or of the teat," which is understood in Abu Zayd's answer). He said: "What is due in legal alms (zakat) for a hundred lamps?" He replied: "Two full-grown mature she-camels, O my friend" (misbah, a lamp, and also a she-camel that rises at day-break from her resting-place, to go to the pasturing ground). He replied: "But if one owns ten daggers?" He replied: "Let him bring out two sheep without grumbling" (khanajir, pl. of khanjar, a dagger, or long knife, and also of khanjar, or khanjur, "a camel rich in milk"). He said: "But if he give over to the slanderer (informer) the best of his kindred?" He replied: "Ay, happy tidings on him on the day of resurrection" (namimah, the foremost of one's relations, and also "the choicest part of one's property"; sa'i, an informer, or slanderer, and also "the collector of the *zakat"*). He said: "Is it that the bearers of sins [burdens] deserve a share in the legal alms?" He replied: "Yea, if they be engaged in warfare for the faith" (*auzar,* pl. of *wizr,* sins, burdens, and also "arms, weapons"). He said: "Is it allowed to the Hajj (pilgrim) to perform the *'umrah* (ceremonies of the lesser pilgrimage)?" He replied: "Nay, nor that he put on a veil" (*ya'tamir,* he performs the *'umrah,* and also "he puts on the *'imarah,"* a kind of headgear or turban). He said: "Is it then open to him to kill a brave one?" He replied: "Yea, as he may kill a wild beast" (*shuja',* a valiant man, and also "a kind of serpent"). He said: "But what about him who has killed a female flutist in the Harem?" He replied: "On him is due the sacrifice of some head of cattle" (*zammarah,* a female player on the *mizmar,* flute, or pipe, and also an ostrich, whose cry is called *zimmar; haram,* the harem, and also "the sacred precinct of Mecca"). He said: "But when he has thrown [his lance] at the leg of a free man and killed him?" He replied: "Let him bring out a sheep in compensation for it" (*saq,* a leg, *hurr,* a freeman; *saqu hurrin,* "the male of the turtle-dove"). He said: "How then if he has killed the mother of 'Auf after donning the pilgrim-cloak?" He replied: "Let him give in alms a small quantity of food" (*umm 'Auf,* name of a woman by her son, and also "a locust"). He said: "Is it incumbent upon the Hajj to be provided with a boat?" He replied: "Yea, so that he may lead them to the watering-places" (*qarib,* a kind of boat, and also "a seeker of water at night-time"). He said: "And what sayest thou about the lawless after the Sabbath?" He replied: "He has done what is lawful at that time" (*haram,* unlawful, opp. to *halal,* lawful, and also "one who dons the pilgrim-cloak, a pilgrim"; *sabt,* Sabbath, and also "shaving of the head"; *hall,* "he has doffed the cloak," which, of course, is a lawful action after the pilgrimage is completed). He said: "But what sayest thou with regard to the sale of a bay?" He replied: "It is unlawful, as the sale of a dead body" *(kumait,* a bay horse, and also "red wine"). He said: "Is it allowed to sell [barter] vinegar for the flesh of the camel?" He said: "Not either for the flesh of sheep" *(khall,* vinegar, and also a camel two years old, or the young of a pregnant camel, the sale of a living animal for flesh, whether of the same kind or any other being unlawful). He said: "Is the sale of a present lawful?" He said: "Nay, nor that of wine" *(hadiyyah,* a present, and also an animal being led to the Ka'beh for sacrifice; *sabiyyah,* a female slave taken from the infidels, and also "wine"). He said: "What sayest thou with regard to the sale of a cornelian stone (or of the hair of a new-born)?" He said: "It is forbidden, in truth" *('aqiqah,* a single cornelian stone; the first wool of an animal, or the hair of a new-born child; but also "an animal sacrificed for a child on the seventh day after its birth"). He said: "Is the sale of (meaning on the part of) a crier to a herdsman allowed?" He replied: "Nay, nor to a collector of the zakat" *(da'i,* one who calls, or makes proclamation, and also "the remainder of milk in the udder," which it is as unlawful to sell as the foetus of an animal in the womb). He said: "May a hawk be sold for dates?" He replied: "Nay, by the Lord of creation and command" *(saqar,* a hawk, and also "date-sugar"). He said: "May a Moslem buy the plunder [taken] from Moslem women?" He replied: "Yea, and it may be inherited from him, when he has died" *(salab,* plunder, booty, and also the bark of a tree, and "leaf or blade of the plant *sumam"*). He said: "But is it allowed that the intercessor be sold?" He replied: "What is there to hinder it?" *(shafi',* an intercessor, and also "a sheep which one buys to skin it"). He said: "May a pitcher be sold to the Benu Asfar?" He replied: "It is abominated as the selling of a helmet [to them]" *(ibriq,* a pitcher, and also a furbished and well-tempered sword; Benu Asfar are the Greeks, to whom, as enemies of Islam, it would be unlawful to sell weapons of attack or defence). He said: "Is it lawful for a man to sell the colt of his camel born in summer?" He replied: "Nay, but he may sell his friend" *(saifi,* a camel colt born in summer, and also "a son begotten in old age," to which latter meaning Abu Zayd's answer refers; *safi,* a milch camel yielding a copious flow, and also "a sincere friend," the meaning which would suggest itself most readily to the ordinary hearer). He said: "But if one has bought a slave and a wound appears on his mother?" He said: "There is no sin in returning him" *(umm,* mother, and also "the pia mater of the brain"). He said: "Holds the right of pre-emption good for the co-partner in a field?" He replied: "Nay, nor for the co-partner in a [yellow] she-camel" *(sahra,* a field, and also "an ass whose white is mingled with grey; *safra,* a yellow she-camel, a word which, however, would more readily suggest the word "bile"). He said: "Is it lawful that the water of the well and of an open place should be heated?" He replied: "If they are in deserts, then certainly not" *(yuhma,* it is being heated, and also "it is prohibited from general use"; *khala,* an open place, here taken in construction with *ma',* water, and also "fodder, both green and dry"). He said: "What sayest thou with regard to the dead body of an infidel (as an article of food)?" He replied: "It is lawful for the dweller in a place and the traveller" *(kafir,* an infidel, and also "the sea"; *maitah,* dead body, and also "fish floating on the water"). He said: "Is it allowed to offer as a forenoon sacrifice squinting men?" He replied: "This is worthier of acceptance" *(al-hul,* pl. of *ahwal,* squint-eyed, and also of *ha'il,* "a sheep that has not conceived"). He said: "May then a divorced woman be sacrificed in the forenoon?" He replied: "Yea, and the nightfarer may be treated thereto hospitably" *(at-taliq,* divorced woman, and also "a she-camel allowed to pasture freely"). He said: "How then if one slaughters before the appearance of the gazelle?" He replied: "It is a sheep whose flesh may be sold (not a sacrifice) undoubtedly" *(al-ghazalah,* gazelle, and also a name for the rising sun, corresponding to *al-jaunah,* which is a name of the sun when setting, as in the words of the poet: *tabadara 'l-jaunatu an taghiba,* the sun was setting quickly). He said: "Is it lawful to make gain by beating wool (or hammering metals)?" he said: "This is like gambling with dice, there is no difference" *(tarq,* beating, hammering, and also "the throwing of pebbles for the purpose of vaticination"). He said: "May one standing say *salam 'alek* to one sitting?" He replied: "It is forbidden between strangers" *(al-qa'id,* one who sits, and also "a woman who has ceased being menstruous or copulating"). He said: "May a sensible man sleep under a fool?" He said: "How lovely it is to do so in the Baqi'" *(raqi',* a fool, and also "the sky"; *al-baqi',* the cemetery of Medina). He said: "Is a Zimmi forbidden to kill an old woman?" He replied: "It is not allowed to oppose him with regard to wine" *(al-'ajuz,* an old woman, and also "old wine," which to kill means to mix it with water [see the Assembly at Tiflis]). He said: "Is it allowed that a man should remove [secede] from his father's premises?" He replied: "It is not allowed either to one obscure or to a noble of birth" *('imarah,* building, edifice, and also "tribe"). He said: "What sayest thou with regard to becoming a Jew?" He replied: "This is the key to an ascetic life" *(tahawwud,* turning a Jew, and also "Turning to God in repentance," according to the words of the Koran, "behold we have returned to thee"). He said: "What sayest thou with regard to patience in misfortune?" He replied: "What a great sin it is!" *(sabr,* patience, and also "tying, fastening, keeping one imprisoned until death ensues"; *baliyyah,* calamity, misfortune, and also "a camel tied to the tomb of her master," and neither watered nor fed until she dies, on which the deceased man was by the Arabs of the ignorance supposed to ride to his doom). He said: "Is it lawful to beat the

ambassador?" He replied: "Yea, and also to load
therewith the seeker of counsel" *(safir,* envoy,
ambassador, and also "leaves falling from a tree";
mustashir, one who asks advice from another, and also
"a fat camel," or "a camel which knows the pregnant
from one that has not conceived"). He said: "May a
man beat his father?" He replied: "The dutiful does so
and refuseth not" *('azzur,* he chastised, beat violently,
and also "he helped, strengthened, honoured," as in
Koran, xlviii. 9, "and may assist him and honour
him"). He said: "What sayest thou with regard to him
who has impoverished his brother?" He replied: "Well
done of him, how brotherly he has acted towards him"
(afqar, he impoverished, and also "he lent a camel to
ride upon her back"). He said: "But what if he strips
his child of its clothing?" He replied: "On what a
handsome thing he has resolved!" *('arahu,* he stripped
him, and also "he gave him the fruit of a date-tree for a
year"). He said: "What then if he bakes his slave on the
fire?" He replied: "There is no sin on him, nor any
blame" *(al-mamluk,* a white slave, and also "a dough
kneaded repeatedly until it has become consistent").
He said: "Is it allowed for a woman to cut her
husband?" (in the Arabic idiom meaning to be unduti-
ful to him). He replied: "Nobody forbids her doing so"
(ba'l, a husband, and also "a date-tree," in which sense
"cutting" may be taken literally, or in the meaning of
"gathering its fruit"). He said: "May then a woman be
upbraided for being bashful?" He replied: "Most certainly" *(khajal,* being bashful, blushing, and also
"being over-bearing in possession of riches," according
to the saying of Mohammed to the women: "When ye
are hungry ye fawn, and when ye have your fill ye
become over-bearing"). He said: "What sayest thou
with regard to him who has shaved [planed] the
tamarisk of his brother?" He replied: "He has sinned
even if he has given permission to him" *(nahata aslat-
hu,* he shaved his tamarisk, and also "he backbited him

and detracted from his honour"). He said: "Is it allowed to the magistrate to appoint a curator for one possessed of a bullock?" He replied: "Yea, to be safe from the mischief of violence" *(saur,* a bullock, and also "madness"). He said: "But is it open to him to strike on the hand of an orphan?" He replied: Yea, until he is of age" *(zaraba 'ala yadi-hi,* besides having the literal meaning given above, is an idiom for: "he appointed a curator for him"). He said: "Is it then allowed to him to take for the same (an orphan) a suburban place?" He replied: "Nay, even if he consents to it" *(ranz,* buildings outside the walls of a city, and also "a wife"). He said: "But when may he (the magistrate) sell the body of an idiot?" He replied: "Whenever he sees that it pleases him" *(badan,* body, and also "a short armour"). He said: "Is it then allowed that he buy for him jakes?" He replied: "Yea, if they be not haunted" *(hashsh,* a privy, and also "a palm-plantation"). He said: "Is it allowed that the magistrate be an oppressor?" He replied: "Yea, if he be knowing" *(zalim,* one who oppresses, and also "one who drinks milk before it curdles"). He said: "Is one fit to become a Kadi who has no perspicacity?" He replied: "Yea, if his conduct be fair" *(basirah,* sharpsightedness, sagacity, and also "a shield"). He said: "But if he is bare of intellect?" He replied: "This is an indication [the title-page] of excellence" *('aql,* intellect, wisdom, and also "embroidered silk stuff"). He said: "But if he have the pride of a tyrant?" He replied: "There is nothing to be said against or to make much of" *(zahw,* pride, and also "a date which begins to colour"; *jabbar,* a tyrant, a shedder of blood, and also "a high palm-tree whose fruit is out of the reach of the hand," opposed to *qa'id).* He said: "Is it allowed that the witness be a suspected character?" He replied: "Yea, if he be a sensible man" *(murib,* suspected, exposed to doubt, and also "one who has plenty of curdled milk"). He said: "But when it has transpired that he has committed sodomy?" He replied: "He is like one who has tailored" *(lat* he committed the sin of the people of Lot, and also "he coated a well with clay"). He said: "And if it comes out that he has been winnowing?" He replied: "Let his evidence be refused, and not accepted" *(gharbal,* he sifted corn, and also "he killed," as the poet says in the metre rejez: "Thou wilt see the kings slain around him." The word has also an obscene meaning). He said: "But if it has become manifest that he is a liar?" He replied: "That is for him a quality which adorns him" *(man, yamin,* he lied, and also, with aor. *yamun,* "he provided for his family"). He said: "What is incumbent upon a servant of God?" He replied: "Let him make oath by the God of creation" *('abid al-haqq,* a servant of God, and also "one who gainsays the true belief," as some commentators explain the word in Koran, xliii. 81). He said: "And what sayest thou with regard to him who has deliberately gouged the eye of a nightingale?" "Let his eye be gouged, to make the speech short" *(bulbul,* a nightingale, and also "a spare man"). He said: "But if he has wounded the Kata (bird) of a woman and death ensued?" He said: "Soul for soul, if it has gone" *(qata',* sandgrouse, and also "what lies between the hip-bones"). He said: "But if a pregnant woman has dropped her foetus in consequence of his blow?" He replied: "Let him atone for his sin by the manumission of a slave" *(hashish,* grass, green herbs, etc., and also "a foetus dropped in abortion"). He said: "What is due in law to one who keeps himself secluded?" He replied: "To have his extremities cut off for the sake of determent" *(mukhtafi,* one who sticks to a place without leaving it, and also "a spoiler of tombs, a stripper of gravecloths"). He said: "What then is to be done to him who has stolen the snakes of the house?" He replied: "Let his right hand be cut off, if they are worth the fourth part of a dinar" *(asawid,* pl. of *aswad,* snakes, and also "household utensils, as a washing-tub,

kettle, dish," etc.). He said: "But if he have stolen a
great worth [value] of gold?" He replied: "There is no
amputation as though he had committed a violent
robbery" *(samin,* what is precious, valuable, and also
"the eighth part," as *nasif* is used for *nisf,* half, *sadis*
for *suds,* sixth part, etc.; under gold is in this case to be
understood a gold coin). He said: "What then if theft is
brought home to a woman?" He replied: "There is no
guilt upon her, and she has nothing to fear" *(saraq,*
theft, and also "white silk"). He said: "Is a marriage
contract valid, which is not witnessed by starlings?"
He replied: "Nay, by the Creator, the Maker" *(qawari,*
pl. of *qariyah,* a bird of the starling kind, from which
the Arabs take a lucky augury, especially with regard
to rain, and also "witnessess," because they follow up
matters, from *qara,* he followed up). He said: "What
sayest thou with regard to a bride who has passed the
first night of a month, and then has been returned early
in the morning to her previous state?" He replied:
"Half of the dowry is due to her, and the days of
probation for divorce *('iddah)* are not incumbent on
her" *(lailah hurrah,* the first night of a month, and also
"a wedding night in which no consummation has taken
place"). Then the asker of the questions said to him:
"Allah has blessed thee with the fullness of a sea that
he who draws from it lessens it not, and of a man of
learning to whose praise the praiser reaches not."
Thereupon he looked down with the downward look of
the abashed, and stopped silent with the silence of the
tongue-tied. Said to him Abu Zayd: "Go on, Sirrah,
how long then [wilt thou tarry], how long?" He replied:
"There remains no missile in my quiver, and after the
breaking forth of thy morn there is no scope left for
debate: by Allah then, the son of what country art
thou, and how beautiful was that which thou hast
expounded." Forthwith he indited with a glib tongue
and a powerful voice:

"In the world I am a pattern, point of sight [Kiblah] for folk of wisdom,
Save that all my days I pass in tardy rest and early outset,
And the stranger, though in Eden he alight, is like one homeless."

Then he said: "O Allah, as Thou hast made us of the number of those who are guided so that they may guide others, make us also of the number of those who follow the right way and spend." Thereupon the people brought him a drove of camels together with a singing girl, and begged him to visit them while after while. Then he rose to go, making them longing for his return, and carrying off the slave-girl and the drove. Thereupon I accosted him and said: "I know thee a rogue, since when then hast thou become a legist?" He kept twisting about a little while and then he indited, saying:

"I alter my coat to the whims of each moment and mix with its changes of welfare and ill-fare,
And pledge my companion in converse with all that may flatter his humour to please my companion,
With tellers of tales circulating narrations, with drinkers of wine circulating the goblets.
Now making the tears by my sermon to pour down, now cheering the hearts by my jocular sallies,
And feasting the ears, if but op'ning my mouth, by spell of my speech that will meeken the restive,
And if I am minded my hand makes the pen drop a shower of pearls to adorn many volumes.
How many a subtlety dim as Soha that came to be bright as a sun by my clearing,
How many my sayings that captivate hearts, and leave in the hearer a yearning behind them,
And virgin Kasidehs indited by me, that met with applause loud expressed and enduring.
Yet plotting of fortune has singled me out, a plotting surpassing that Tir'aun's 'gainst Moses,

And kindles against me a war day by day, I tread through its blaze on a furnace, a furnace!

And strikes me with ills, such as melt a man's vigour, and blanch people's heads with the whiteness of hoar-frost.

And brings to me near but the alien, the hateful, while banishing from me the nearest, the dearest!

And were it not but for the vileness of fortune my lot in the world were not vile, by its fell feud."

Then I said to him: "Soothe thy sorrows and blame not fortune, but be thankful to Him who has turned thee from the way of Iblis to the way of Idris" (Ash-Shafi'i). He replied: "Leave off idle talk, and tear no veils, but rise with us to make for the Masjid of Yathrib (Medina), haply we may cleanse away by the visitation the filth of our sins." So I said: "Far be it that I fare with thee, before I learn thy explanation." He replied: "By Allah, thou hast imposed duties upon me, and when thou hast asked, thou hast asked but a small matter; listen then to what remedies the mind, and removes ambiguity." Then after he had made clear to me the enigmatical and lifted from me my perplexity, we tightened our saddles, and I fared on, and he fared on, while he ceased not from his nightly talk as long as the journey lasted, on such topics that made me forget hardship and I would have liked with him "the distance to be long" (allusion to Koran, ix. 42, "but the distance seemed long to them," referring to those who were called upon to join in the expedition to Tabuk), until when we had reached the city of the Prophet, and obtained our desire from the visitation, he set out Syriawards, and I towards Iraq, he veered to the West, and I to the East.

THE THIRTY-THIRD ASSEMBLY

THE ENCOUNTER AT TIFLIS

I had covenanted with Allah, (be He exalted) since I was of the age of about a score, that I would not delay prayer as far as it was in my power, so that with my roaming in deserts, and in spite of the sport of leisure-hours, I kept the stated times of prayer and guarded myself from the sin of letting them slip by. When I joined a caravan, and alighted at any place, I welcomed the summoner to prayer, and took my pattern from him who observed it religiously.

Now, it happened that at a time when I had come to Tiflis, I prayed together with a number of poorly-off people, and when we had finished our prayers and were about to go an old man in worn garments with a face contorted by the palsy came to us, and said: "I conjure him who has been made of the clay of liberality, and suckled of the milk of good fellowship, that he but spare me a moment's hurrying, and listen to a few words from one who is at the end of his strength." Then the people stopped to listen further, and waited silently for what he might say.

Now, when he perceived how nicely they kept quiet, and how considerate they showed themselves to be, he began: "O you, endowed with eye clear of sight, and visions of bright perception, does not eye-witnessing dispense with hearsay? Does not the smoke tell of the fire? Gray hairs are apparent, and weakness oppressive, and disease manifest, and the inward state thus laid bare. Yet once I was one of those who possess and bestow, who exercise authority and rule, who grant help and give gifts, who assist and assault. But calamities ceased not to subvert, nor viccissitudes to take away scrap by scrap, till the nest was spoiled, and the palm empty, privation became my raiment and bitterness my life-stay. My little ones whined from hunger and craved for the sucking of even a date-stone. Yet I came not to stand in this place of ignominy to disclose things to you which should be hidden, but after I had suffered and was palsy-stricken and had waxed gray from all I had met with, oh! would that I had not been spared!" He sighed, and continued with a feeble voice: "I cry to the Compassionate, praise be to Him, for fortune's fickleness and hostile rancour, and for calamities that have shattered my rock, and over-thrown my fame and its foundations, have broken down my stem, and woe to him, whose boughs adver-sities pull down and break!

"My dwellings they have wasted even as to banish from the wasted spot the rats themselves: they left me bewildered and dazed, to bear the brunt of poverty and its pangs, while before I was a lord of wealth, who trailed his skirts along in luxury, whose leaves the supplicants beat freely down, whose hospitable glowing night-fires all night-farers praised; but who is now as though the world, that casts the evil eye on him, had never smiled, from whom one turns who was his visitor, and whom one scorns to know who once sought his gift. So if a good man mourns the evil plight he sees an old man in, betrayed by fortune, then let him ease the sorrow that afflicts him, and mend the state that puts him thus to shame."

Now the company was inclined to ascertain his con-dition, so as to find out what was the truth of the matter and to sift his affair. So they said to him "We know by this time the excellence of your degree, and the abundance of your raincloud, but make now known to us the tree of your branch, and withdraw the veil from your descent."

Then he showed himself reluctant, with the reluctance of one on whom misfortunes have fallen (or to whom the tidings of daughters born to him have been brought), and he said in a low voice: "By your life, I assure you, the branch does not show by the zest of its fruit from what root it has sprung, so eat what is sweet, when it comes to hand, and ask not the honey where the bee has swarmed! And learn to discern, when you have pressed the grapes, the must of your press from the acid it yields, that by testing you value the costly and cheap, to buy and to sell all things by their like; for blame would accrue to the witty and the wise if error of judgement were fastened upon them."

The people were by now roused by his sagacity and subtleness, and beguiled by the beauty of his delivery, along with pity for his disease, and so they collected for him from the treasure at their belts, saying "You have drifted to a shallow well and arrived at an empty hive; so take this trifling pittance and reckon it neither a miss nor a hit." Then he made much of their little, and accompanied its acceptance with thanks, and dragged himself away, stumbling on his road. Now I thought somehow he had disguised his appearance, and shammed in his gait, so I rose to track his traces, and thread his path, while he gave me a wide berth. After a while however, he became aware I was following him, and he turned to look at me with the look of him that is friendly and glad of the meeting, saying to me "I imagine you are a brother of peregrination, and looking for companionship. Would you then have a mate who is kind to you and helps you, and is indulgent with you and shares expenses?" Said I, "If such a mate came forward, Providence indeed would favour me!" He replied "You have found one, so rejoice, you have encountered the generous, so join him."

Then he gave a long laugh, and stood before me, a sound man, Shaykh Abu Zayd of Seruj, with no ailment in his body, and nothing doubtful about his outward tokens. Then I was once again most happy to see him, and was glad he was not stricken with the palsy in reality, yet when I thought I ought to rebuke him for the evilness of his ways, was in two minds. But before I could chide him, he opened his mouth and said: "I show myself in rags, so that people might say 'There is a wretch that forbears with the hardship of the times'. I feign to the world to be palsied in face, for often my heart thus obtained its wish; aye, for my raggedness I find compassion and for my palsy I meet my wants."

Then he added "There is no pasture for me in these parts, nor anything to be hoped for from these people, and if you will be my companion, let us go upon our way!" So we fared forth from that place, the two of us, and I kept company with him for about two years; in fact I would have kept company with him while my life lasted, but time, the disperser, forbade me.

THE THIRTY-FOURTH ASSEMBLY

THE ENCOUNTER AT ZABID

When I crossed the desert as far as Zabid, I had with me a slave whom I had reared up to his full age, and trained until he had perfected his right conduct. He was fully familiar with my ways, and knew how to draw forth my goodwill, so as not to overstep my intentions, nor to be remiss in carrying out my wishes. His good services won my heart, and I valued him greatly, singling him out as companion both in travel and at home.

But pernicious fate made away with him, and I was without a servant for at least a year after his death, without relishing my food, until the various inconveniences of solitary life, and the troubles of getting up and sitting down, drove me to take the bead instead of the pearl, and to look for one who might be a stopgap for my needs.

So I repaired to the slave-sellers, in the market of Zabid, and I said "I want a lad who will give satisfaction when he is tried, and who is approved of when he is tested, and let him be one of those whom the intelligent have reared, and poverty alone has thrown into the market."

Then every one of them bestirred himself for the object of my search, and bustled about in order to encompass it speedily and to his own advantage. Three new moons completed their round, and turned in their increase and wane, but nothing happened of their promises, and no thundercloud yielded rain.

Now, when I saw that the slave-merchants had

forgotten or had pretended to forget, I knew that not everyone who undertakes a work carries it through, and that nothing will scratch my skin as well as my own nail. I abandoned the way of commissioning, and sallied forth to the market with the yellow coin and the white ones, and had the slave-boys led past me, inquiring for the prices, when lo! there accosted me a man who had a face-veil drawn well over his nostrils, and who held a boy by the forearm, saying:

"Who buys from me a lad who proves deft at this work, and is in make and manners surpassing fair? Equal to any task you may lay upon him, who speeds to you when you speak, and when spoken to, attends; who, if you stumble says to you "Rise to your feet," and if you bid him enter the fire, he enters it; who, when you will, attends upon you, and is contented with but a scrap, if such is your wish. Although he has collected his wits, when he talks, he neither tells a lie nor claims more than his due. He does not yield to the call of any wish of his own, nor lets a secret trusted with him, get out of keeping. Oft-times he makes one wonder at his skill, excelling both in verse and prose, alike, and were it not for life's straitening stress, and little ones that sadly need clothing and food, by God, I would not sell him for the realms that Kusrau rules!"

Now when I looked at the boy's straight build, and his exquisite beauty, I fancied him to be one of the youths of the Garden of Delights, and said "This is not a man, but surely an honoured angel." I asked him to announce his name, not from a desire to know it, but to see whether his elocution matched his looks, and how his utterance responded to the fairness of his face. But he spoke neither bitter nor sweet, and uttered not a sound which would have marked him either as the son of a slave or a woman who was free-born. So I turned aside from him and said "Well, be gone!" Then he burst into a laugh, and nodding his head to me said "O you (whose wrath is kindled if I only withhold my name) do not seem to be a man who in his dealings would be fair. But if you are not pleased until it is revealed, then I will say that I am Joseph, I am Joseph, I say."

He thus allayed my anger, and made me think of the story of Joseph and his beauty, in the Koran; and I asked his master his price. "His price is low," said the old man, "and his keep is little, and I wish above all to make you fond of the lad by lightening the price, so weigh out two hundred dirhems, if you will, and be thankful to me as long as you live." So I paid him the amount at once, and it did not occur to my mind that everyone who sells cheap makes one pay dear. When the transaction was concluded, the eyes of the lad brimmed over, and he said to his old master "Allah confound you! Is it right to sell such a one as me just to fill hungry bellies, and is it walking in the path of justice to make me bear what cannot be endured? To try me sore with terror after terror though one like me, if tried, cannot easily be frightened? Yet you have probed me and experienced from me good counsels, unalloyed with any falsehoods. How often have you set me as a snare for game, and I brought home prey caught in my net. You imposed on me tasks that were difficult but I always obeyed, though I might have well refused them. How many a battle I had to fight in, how much booty, and I had no share; and never, in all my days, did I sin, which if you break with me, could be revealed. Nor could you stumble on a fault of mine, praise be to God, to hide or proclaim it. Can you cast me off so lightly, as women cast off their worn shreds? Why does your soul allow you to enslave me and offer me for sale as goods are sold? Would you not shield my honour, as I shield my own concerns the day when parting grieves us, and say to him that barters for me 'This is not to buy or borrow?' "

When the old man had heard this, he fetched a deep sigh, and wept, and said to me "I hold this lad in the place of my son, and distinguish him not from the lobes of my liver, and were it not for the emptiness of my house and the extinction of my lamp, he would not leave me until he had escorted my bier. Now you have seen what the pangs of separation have done to him, and the Believer is kind and gentle. So, if you would have a mind for the soothing of his heart, and the removal of his grief, to stipulate with me for the cancelling of the sale, whenever I ask for it, and not to find me importune if I should press for it, for it is among the choice traditions transmitted by the Trustworthy, that "he who grants redemption to one repenting of his bargain, Allah remits to him his transgressions." Said I: "I will make you that promise, prompted by shame, indeed," but in my heart I thought otherwise. Then he asked the boy to approach him, and kissed him beteen the eyes, saying, while his tears were starting, "Bear patiently, my soul may be your ransom, what you have met of sorrow and of anguish; may the parting not last for long, nor flag the beast that brings us to reunion; through the aid of God, the Mighty, the Creator."

Then he said to him: "I commend you to the keeping of one who is a good master," and tucked his skirt and turned away. But the boy remained sobbing and wailing until the other might have gone the length of a mile, and stopped the flow of his tears at last, saying "Do you know for what I have wept, and what was my object?" I said "I suppose it is the separation from your master that made you weep so." Said he: "You are in one valley, and I am in another, and what a distance there is between a wisher and his wish." Then he went on: "By Allah, weeping as I did was not for a departed friend, but for a fool, whose eyes, though open, lead him into pitfalls. So that he came to grief, and was sadly disgraced, and lost his white engraven coin, his yellow too. Have not these words warned you enough that I was free, and therefore not for sale at all? For clear as daylight should it be that was what *Joseph* meant!"

Now I looked at his speech as something seen in the mirror of one who jests, or the exhibition of one indulging in pleasure; so we jostled about in altercation which led us to an appeal to the judge.

When we explained the case to the Kadi, and read to him the chapter and verse of our case, he said "Indeed, he who has warned has excused himself, he who has put one on one's guard is like one who has given information; he who has made one see the state of affairs, has done no damage. Now what you both have said in explanation, demonstrates that this lad has tried to rouse you, but you would not be awakened, and has advised you, but you would not understand; therefore veil the ailment of your stupidity and hide it, and blame yourself, and do not blame him. Beware that you do not lay your hand on him, for he is free of body, and not subject to be exposed for sale as a slave. It was only yesterday that his father brought him into my presence, a little while before sunset, declaring him to be his branch, that he had grown, and that he had no heir but him." Then I said to the Kadi: "And do you know his father? May Allah put him to shame!" He replied "How should Abu Zayd be unknown for whose wound there is no retaliation, and of whom every Kadi has stories to tell and proclamation to make." Then I gnashed my teeth in anger and said "There is no power and no strength but in Allah the Exalted, the Great!" becoming wide awake, but the time had slipped when I should have known it. So my mishap made me cast down my looks, and I swore that I would never again deal with the wearer of a face-veil as long as I lived, bewailing all the time my losing, and the shame I would be put to regarding it among my comrades. Then the Kadi said to me (when he saw my distress and became aware of the brunt of my burning grief) "Your loss has given you a lesson, and he who has roused your wits has not done you an injury. Take, then, warning by your adventure, and conceal it from your friends; remember always what has occurred to you, so as to keep in mind the admonition which your money has administered to you, and mould yourself after the disposition of one who has profited by the examples set before him."

Thereupon I took leave of him, donning the raiment of shame and sorrow and trailing my skirt of defrauded folly. I proposed to show Abu Zayd my aversion by shunning him, and to cut him for the remainder of my life, deliberately keeping aloof from his abode, and avoiding him. But he came upon me in a narrow path, and welcomed me with the welcome of an affectionate friend, though all I did was to frown at him and keep silent.

Then he said "What ails you that you turn up your nose at me?" I answered: "Have you forgotten that you plotted against me and cheated me, and did the thing which you have done?" Then he said "O you who show estrangement and curl up your lip in savage scowl, and feather the shaft of blame that hits as hard, nay harder than sharp arrows, and say that he who sells a free-born man, as a dusty nag is sold, O cut short your say, and know that I am not the first to have done this, as you seem to think; his tribe sold Joseph thus, though the people knew who they were. So it is, and by the Holy House that is visited, and those who circumambulate it, emaciated, with ashen locks, I would not have stood in this place of shame, I swear it, if I owned a coin. So excuse your brother, and bother not with the blame of one who ignores the facts."

Then he added: "My excuse is plain and your dirhems are gone. But your shrinking from me and your aversion to me arises from the excess of your tender concern for the remainder of your pelf; if you are cross, and give way to your stinginess, in order to escape the bait that hangs in my nets, the mourning women will weep over your wits."

He thus deluded me by his deceitful utterance and his powerful sorcery into turning his friend and becoming attached to him again, flinging the remembrance of his exploit behind me, as if it were some abominable thing.

THE THIRTY-FIFTH ASSEMBLY

THE ENCOUNTER AT SHIRAZ

In Shiraz I met with such an Assembly, which invited a passer-by to stay, even if he were in a hurry, that I was unable to tear myself away from them; my foot could not move to step past them, I was so drawn to them. I thought that it would be most interesting to test their intrinsic worth, and see how their fruit would be from their blossom.

Now, they proved to be most select people, and he who inclined to them was profited, and while we were engaged in talk pleasanter than the milk of grapes, or the song of the birds there entered in our midst a man in two tattered pieces of clothing who had well nigh reached the end of life. He greeted us with a glib tongue, and expressed himself in the delivery of the eloquent. He sat down as one joining the assembly, with his hands round his knees and said "O Allah, let us be of the rightly guided!"

Now, the people made little of him, as he was so poorly attired, forgetting that they would have to deal with the two things smallest in him, his tongue and his heart, and they began to bandy between them the chapter of rhetoric, counting its aloes as common wood. He said not a word at first, nor declared himself by any sign, until he had reckoned up their intellectual powers, deciding which of them made the scale rise and which one weighed it down.

But when he had brought to light their buried treasures and exhausted their quivers, he said: "O people, if you had but known that behind the plug there is pure wine, you would not have slighted a wearer of tattered garments, but asked what parts he possesses." Then he let flow the springs of learning, and let forth marvels of wonderment and what was worthy to be written on fluid gold; and when he had captivated all their senses, he stirred for making his departure and made as if to go. But the company clung to him and barred his way and refused to let him leave, saying "We have seen the colour of your feathers, now make known to us the shell of your egg and its yolk!"

Then he was silent as one choked by tears, and he was pitied by all. When I knew that it was Abu Zayd, and saw that he was defaced in countenance, pitied him; but I concealed his secret once more, as an internal disease is concealed, and veiled his cunning scheme, although he did not think so, until he ceased wailing, and blinked at me with an eye full of laughter, and began: "I crave Allah's forgiveness, humbling myself, for all the sins whose heavy load burdens me. O people, how many old maids keep at home, though in assemblies their virtues were praised; have I not cut down many, not fearing from any heir that might revenge them on me or claim a fine.

"And when the sin was laid at my door, I boldly cleared myself and said: 'It was Fate!' My soul never stopped its headlong career in cutting damsels down, till hoariness shone on the crown of my head and checked me from performing such deeds. So since my temples have turned grey never have I shed any more a maiden's blood, old or young. But now I rear, in spite of what may be seen of my condition and of my slacking trade, a maiden who for a long time has stayed at home, sheltered and cared for – veiled from even the air itself. And she in spite of being so secluded, has wooers for her comeliness and pleasingness. But for her outfit, at the least, I cannot do without a hundred, though I try as I may, while in my hand there is not one silver coin, the ground is empty and the sky yields no rain. Now is there one here who could help me, that I may wed her among the singing-girls' cheering strain? Then let him wash my grief with its proper soap, and cleanse my heart from sorrows that worry me, that he may cull my praises whose fragrancy will only cease to breathe when man prays in vain."

There was none left in that company but his palm opened to help Abu Zayd and when his wish had proved successful, and his hundred was complete, he praised them as beseems the upright, and tucked up his skirt for departure. But I followed him, wishing to learn who was the foster-daughter of his chamber, and whom it was that he had cut down in his early life, and it was as if the swiftness of my rising had made him aware of my intention, for he said: "Listen to me . . . Cutting down means thinning the wine, not a lance or sword killing a man; and the maid kept at home a long time means the daughter of the grape-tree, not a virgin of high extraction; and to wed her to cup and flask was the errand, which you saw me intent upon when I joined you. Understand then what I have said, and decide on kind forbearance, if you will. I am quarrelsome and you are faint-hearted, so there is a wide gulf between us," and he bade me farewell, and went away, making me send after him more than one glance of loving affection.

THE THIRTY-SIXTH ASSEMBLY

THE ENCOUNTER AT MALTIYAH

In this Assembly Abu Zayd proposes twenty riddles or con-
undrums of a particular kind, and all of the same form, which
consists in finding a word resembling a given short sentence in
such a manner that its component parts are synonymous with
the members of the phrase in question. The introduction to the
Assembly itself adduces as an instance the query, what is like *an-
naum fat,* Sleep has departed, to which the answer would be *al-
karamat,* pl. of *karamah* in the sense of "wonder", "miracle",
because the initial part of the word, *al-kara,* means "slumber",
and the final syllable, *mat,* signifies "is dead". The English
reader of this translation will not be worse off than Abu Zayd's
Arabic audience, for the author gives no solution in the body of
the Assembly, leaving its discovery to the ingenuity of the
listener, but if his curiosity and interest are roused by the quaint
form of the questions and the lively style in which they are
introduced, he will find at the cost of small trouble amusement as
well as linguistic instruction in the short commentary, which
Hariri himself has attached to this composition.

I made my camel of foreign travel kneel down at
Maltiyah, and my pouch was at that time well filled
with coin. So I made it my wont, when I had deposed
there my staff, to frequent the places of entertainment
and to hunt after rare pleasures, so that nothing
escaped me worthy to be seen or heard, and no play-
ground or resort of enjoyment was left unvisited by me,
until, when I had no further business there, and no
desire for longer stay, I resolved to expend my remaining gold in buying travelling gear. Now when I had
completed my preparations, and was ready for departure, or all but ready, I saw a group of nine people, who
had purchased some wine, wherewith they had

ascended a hillock, and their winning manners captivated men's eyes, while their pleasantry was sweet-
spoken. Therefore I wended towards them from a wish
to join in their conversation, not in their drinking-bout,
and from eagerness to mix with them, not to taste the
contents of their tumblers. Now when I had become
the tenth in their string, and a companion in their
forenoon meeting, I found them to be a medley
assemblage thrown together from the deserts, though
the woof of literary culture united them as with the
union of relationship, and matched them in their ranks,
so that they shone like the luminaries of the Twins, and
appeared as a community whose members are of one
kindred. So I rejoiced at having been guided to them,
and praised the lucky star that had made me light upon
them, beginning to shake my arrow together with their
arrows, and to solace myself with the perfume of their
refinement, not with that of their wine, until the branch-
roads of discussion led us to the proposing of riddles, as
if thou sayst, intending thereby *al-karamat,* what is like
"al-naum fat" (sleep has departed), which may be
expressed by *"al-kara mat"* (slumber is dead),
whereupon we began to display both Soha (the smallest
star in the Bear) and the moon, and to cull both the
thorn and the fruit, and while we were spreading out
the fresh and the old, and drawing from [fishing out of]
the pot the fat and the lean, an old man intruded upon
us, whose bloom of complexion and beauty of form
had gone, while knowledge and experience remained
with him. Then he stood as one who listens and
observes, picking up what we were scattering, until the
purses were empty and it became obvious that no more
was to be hoped for. Now when he saw the flagging of
their powers [faculties], and that both he who drew
water from the top of the well, and he who drew it from
the bottom, were equally baffled, he gathered his skirts
together, and turned his back on us, saying: "Not
everything black is a date, nor is everything ruddy

wine." Then we clung to him as the chameleon clings to the trees, and blocked his progress as with bars, saying to him: "The cure of a rent is to stitch it, and if not, then retaliation! retaliation! So hope not to wound while thou art safe, and to make bleed the gash while thou goest scot-free." Then he turned his bridle, sitting down in his place for a good stay, and said: "Since you have challenged me to discussion, I shall give the judgement of Solomon in the matter of the sown field. Know, ye owners of literary accomplishments and golden coloured wine, that the proposing of riddles is for the purpose of testing the quickness of wit and bringing out its hidden treasures, under the condition, that they are founded on a real resemblance and contain meaning words, and some scholarly nicety. For if they are of a style different from this they are refuse [worthless], and not to be put into the casket [as something worthy to be preserved], and I noticed that your definitions kept not within these limits, and distinguished not between the acceptable and the objectionable." We said to him: "Thou art right, and hast spoken the truth. But measure out to us somewhat from thy select store, and pour upon us from thy main sea" [ocean]. Said he: "I will do so in a manner that those who failed may not doubt, nor look at me with suspicion." Then he turned to the foremost of the people, and said:

  1. "O thou who excels in sharpness, who strikes the fire-sticks of merit,
  What is it that likens saying: 'hunger is cheered by provisions'?"
Then he smiled to the second, and indited:
  2. "O man of surpassing honour, unsullied by any baseness,
  What is as if one riddling would say: 'a back looked askance at'?"
Then he glanced at the third, saying:

3. "O thou, the children of whose thought resemble coin of ready course,
What is like saying to a man thou pliest with riddles: 'he met a gift'?"

Then he stretched his neck towards the fourth, and said:

4. "O thou who solvest what is intricate of riddles and enigmas,
Reveal to me that which resembles to 'take a thousand gold coins'?"

Then he cast his eye upon the fifth, and said:

5. "O such an one of shrewdest wit, endowed with brightest sagacity,
What resembles 'he who neglects adornment'? If rightly guided, be quick and tell."

Then he turned in the direction of the sixth, and said:

6. "O thou from whose capacity a rival's steps stop short by far,
What is like thy saying to him who joins with thee in riddles: 'Hold in! hold in!'?"

Then he winked his eyebrows towards the seventh, and said:

7. "O thou who own'st intellect of brilliancy, in subtleness high of rank amongst thy friends,
Explain, and, mind, tell aright in doing so, what saying is similar to 'brother fled'?"

Then he bade the eighth to listen, and indited:

8. "O thou whose gardens of excellence are fresh with flowers in bright array,
What is like telling the sharp of wit in solving riddles: 'he chose not silver'?"

Then he cast a glance upon the ninth, and said:

9. "O thou to whom they point for a mind of ready wit and for eloquence,
Expound to us, what is like the speech of the riddler: 'tread upon the crowd'?"

Now when he came at last to me, he patted me on the shoulder saying:

10. "O thou possessed of subtleties to baffle sore
and floor opponents,
Thou makest clear, so tell us what is like my saying:
'be still, my uncle'?"

Then he said: "I have watered you and allowed you
time, and if you want me to let you have another
draught, I let you have it." So the brunt [heat] of thirst
drove us to ask for a second drink. Whereupon he said:
"I am not like one who from selfishness stints his boon-
companions, nor of those whose fat remains in their
own dish." Then he returned to the first, and said:

11. "O thou whose sharpness unfolds a riddle
[unties a ticklish knot], however tight,
If one propose as a riddle, 'take this,' say true what
is like it."

Then he bent his neck towards the second, and said:

12. "O thou whose eloquence appears clear from
his skill in explanation,
What is as if people would say: 'an onager has been
decked out'?"

Then he blinked towards the third, and said:

13. "O thou who in sagacity and sharpness are like
Asma'i,
What is like saying by way of riddle: 'spend lavishly,
thou conquerest then'?"

Then he looked sharp at the fourth, and indited:

14. "O thou who if knotty questions arise enlightens
their darkness,
What is it that likens saying: 'sniff in the perfume of
grape-wine'?"

Then he ogled the fith, and said:

15. "O thou whose intellect lets him not give way to
anxious thoughts and doubt,
What resembles saying to a man expert in riddles:
'shield the ruined'?"

Then he stepped in front of the sixth, and indited:

16. "O thou endowed with sagacity in which thy
perfect worth appears,

The saying, 'he travelled awhile at night,' say what a thing is like to it."

Then he turned his glance towards the seventh, and said:

17. "O thou whose wit, brisk of market, gives thee adornment and honour,
Say, for thou art able to tell us, what word is like 'love a coward'?"

Then he looked in the direction of the eighth, and said:

18. "O thou who in fame hast reached a height surpassing every height by far,
What resembles, tell us, saying: 'give a crook [crutch] deprived of the handle-part'?"

Then he smiled to the ninth, and said:

19. "O thou who hold'st undoubtedly fine judgement and elocution,
What is like saying to the skilled in solving riddles: 'I own the bullock'?"

Then he clutched my sleeve, and said:

20. "O thou who has penetrating sharpness of wit in solving intricate question, bright as a star,
What is resembling the saying: 'whiz of a muzzle'? Explain so that thy expounding renders it clear."

Now when he had delighted us with what we had heard, and challenged us to disclose its meaning, we answered: "We are not of the horses of this racecourse, and our hands are not equal to untying these knots; so if thou wilt explain, thou conferest a favour, and if thou wilt keep it hidden, thou inflictest grief." Then he consulted his mind for and against and shook both his arrows (of consent or refusal), until he was pleased to vouchsafe the bounty, coming forward to the company, and saying: "O ye people of eloquence and distinction, I will forthwith make known to you that which you know not, and thought not you would ever know, so fasten upon it your vessels and freshen therewith the assemblies." Then he began an explanation which furbished the intellects, and withal emptied the sleeves (breast pockets), until the understandings became brighter than the sun, and the pockets as if yesterday they had not been rich. Now when he bethought himself of departure, he was asked about his abode. Then he sighed as sigheth the bereft mother, and said:

Each mountain-path is path for me, and ample is my dwelling there,
Save that for Seruj town my heart is crazed with longing, mad with love.
She is my virgin land from whence my erewhile youthful breeze has sprung,
And for her mead so rich of growth above all meads I fondly yearn.
Afar from her no sweet is sweet to me, delightful no delight."

Thereupon I said to my companions, "This is Abu Zayd, the Seruji, whose riddles are the least of his elegancies," and I began to descry to them the beauty of his diction, and the obedience of speech to his will. Then I turned round, and lo! he had leaped up, and was gone with what he had gained. So we wondered at his performance, when he had fallen in our midst, and knew not whither he had wended and swerved.

EXPLANATION OF THE RIDDLES

1. *Hunger is cheered by provisions (ju unmidd bizad)* resembles *tawamir,* pl. of *tamur,* books, rolls, scrolls (= *tawa,* hunger, + *mir,* pass. of *mar,* has been provided for).

2. *A back (which is) looked askance at (zahr asabathu 'ain)* resembles *mata'in,* pl. of *mat'un,* pierced with a lance (= *mata,* back, + *'in,* pass. of *'an,* is struck by the evil eye).

3. *He met a gift (sadaf ja'izah)* resembles *al-fasilah,* fem. of *al-fasil,* what separates two things (= *alfa,* he found, + *silah,* a gift).

4. *Take a thousand gold coins (tanawal alf dinar)* resembles *hadiyah,* fem. of *hadi,* one who guides aright (= *ha,* take, + *diyah,* fine for bloodshed which amounts to 1,000 dinars).

5. *He neglects adornment (ahmal hilyah)* resembles *al-ghashiyah,* a saddle-cloth (= *algha,* he disregarded, + *shiyah,* finery).

6. *Hold in! hold in! (ukfuf, ukfuf)* resembles *mahmah,* a desert (= *mah,* stop, repeated for the sake of emphasis).

7. *Brother fled (ash-shaqiq aflat)* resembles *akhtar,* pl. of *khatar,* dangers (= *akh,* brother, + *tar,* he flew, took to flight).

8. *He chose not silver (ma akhtar fizzah)* resembles *abariqah,* pl. of *ibriq,* pitchers (= *aba* he refused, + *riqah,* a silver coin).

9. *Tread upon a crowd (das jama'ah)* resembles *tafiyah,* fem. of *tafi,* what floats on the water (= *ta,* for *ta',* imp. of *wata',* tread under foot, trample upon, + *fiyah,* for *fi'ah,* a troup of men).

10. *Be still my uncle (khali uskut)* resembles *khalisah,* fem. of *khalis,* pure, sincere (= *khali,* apocopated vocative of *khali,* my maternal uncle, + *sah,* hush!).

11. *Take this (khuz tilk)* resembles *hatik,* this woman (= *ha,* take, as in the 4th riddle, + *tik,* fem. of *zak,* this).

12. *An onager has been decked out (himar wahsh zin)* resembles *farazin,* pl. of *firzan,* Queens in chess (= *fira,* wild ass, + *zin,* pass. of *zan,* he was adorned).

13. *Spend lavishly, thou conquerest then (infaq taqma')* resembles *muntaqim,* one who avenges himself (= *mun,* imp. of *man,* spend on provisions, + *taqim,* aor. of *waqam,* thou subduest).

14. *Sniff in the perfume of grape-wine (istanshi rih*

mudamah) resembles *rahrah,* vast, wide, ample (= *rah,* imp. of *rah,* smell, + *rah,* one of the names of wine).

15. *Shield the ruined (ghatti halka)* resembles *sunbur,* an isolated palm-tree, a word also of various meanings (+ *sun,* imp. of *san,* shelter, protect, preserve, + *bur,* pl. of *ba'ir,* doomed to destruction).

16. *He travelled a while at night (sar bi'l-lail muddah)* resembles *sarahin,* pl. of *sirhan,* wolves (= *sara,* he fared at night, + *hin,* time).

17. *Love a coward (ihbab faruqah)* resembles *miqla',* a sling (= *miq.* imp. of *wamiq,* be in love with, + *la',* timid, pusillanimous).

18. *Give a crock deprived of the handle-part (ati ibriq yaluh bighair 'urwah)* resembles *uskub,* flowing, shed (= *us,* imp. of *as,* bestow, + *kub,* a mug without handle).

19. *I own the bullock (as-saur milki)* resembles *al-laali,* pl. of *lu'lu',* the pearls (= *al-la'a,* the wild ox, + *li,* to me, mine).

20. *Whiz of a muzzle (safir jahfalah)* resembles *mukashafah,* uncovering, disclosing (= *muka,* a whistling sound, produced by blowing into one's hand, + *shafah,* lip).

THE THIRTY-SEVENTH ASSEMBLY

THE ENCOUNTER AT SA'DAH

I travelled to Sa'dah, one of the chief towns of the Yemen, at a time when I was as straight as a spear-shaft and of vigour that outstripped the young of the onager. Now, when I had seen its freshness and feasted my eyes on its meads, I inquired from the most knowing of its informants, whom of lordly persons and mines of excellence it contained, so that I might take one for my beacon in times of darkness, and my tower of strength in days of oppression.

The person who was pointed out to me as composed of these strengths was a Kadi, wide of range in generosity, easy in his circumstances, of the tribe of Temim, and a true Temini in disposition. So by respectfully approaching him, and making myself valuable to him by being chary in visiting, I became the echo of his voice; and while gathering his honey and inhaling the fragrance of his bay-tree, I used to watch the contentions of litigant parties brought before him.

Now, when the Kadi was sitting to give judgement on a day of flocking-together and crowding, there came an old man in plumage much the worse for wear, of very shaky appearance, who looked at the crowd with the eye of the money-sifter. Then he stated that he had an unmanageable adversary, and a lad was brought to the presence as bold as a lion. Said the old man "May Allah help the Kadi, and may he be preserved from ever becoming guilty of connivance! Behold this is my son, like a bad reed-pen or a rusty sword, who ignores the predicaments of equity, and suckles the teats of contradiction and opposition. When I advance, he draws back, when I speak plain, he shuffles in his speech; when I kindle a fire, he puts it out, when I roast meat, he scatters ashes. Although I reared him since he first crawled until he was a youth, and was to him the kindest of educators, still I could not teach him to do things as I did them."

Then the Kadi made much of his complaint, and put great stress upon it, and those around him agreed that it was a case of grave concern.

"I protest that disobedience in children is a great distress," said the Kadi, "and in many an instance infertility keeps the eye cooler."

Said the boy whom this speech had incensed: "By Him who has set up judges for the sake of justice, and possessed them of the reins of preferment and discrimination, he never prayed but I said Amen, and he never made a claim but I maintained its truth, he never struck fire but I gave sparks, in spite of the fact that he is one who craves for eggs from the cock-hawk, and wants camels to fly!"

Then the Kadi said to him: "Then how does he vex you, and force you into disobedience, as he claims?"

"Ever since his substance has gone," replied the boy, "and he has been visited by penury, he urges me to roll my tongue in begging, and to ask rain from the clouds of bounty, so that his draught, which had dried up, might flow afresh in abundance, and what was broken in his fortunes might be set again. Yet, when he first started schooling me he imbued my heart with the notion that inordinate desire is a thing to be blamed, and covetousness worthy of rebuke, that greed breeds indigestion, and begging is a reproach. Then he told me, with all the polish of his verse:

"Content yourself with scanty means, giving thanks, like one who thinks the little much;
Shun greediness, that never fails to lower the worth of anyone who may take to it.

Shield your fair name and hide it with jealous care,
as with a frown a lion would defend his mane.
Bear with patience, and bear poverty, as lords of
holy purpose bore patiently;
Do not spill the waters of your face even if he you
beg from spends on you gifts galore;
For free is he, who, if a mote hurts his eye, conceals
that mote even from his two pupils,
And if his gold is gone to rags does not see his way
to beg."

The old man rushed at his son and growled
"Disobedient one, you choke and stifle me! Woe betide
you, will you teach your nurse how to give suck?
Forsooth, the scorpion had rubbed himself against the
snake, and the newly weaned ones have coursed with
stallions!" Then, as if he had repented of what he had
said, his eye began to look fondly once more upon the
young man and he lowered to him the wing of the
kindly, and spoke. "Alas, dear son, those who are
bidden to be contented, and chidden from self-
abasement are the owners of merchandise, and the
workers of gain through handicraft, but as for those
who are possessed of needs, an exception is made on
their behalf with regard to prohibited matters. Granted
you were ignorant of this interpretation, and it has not
reached you yet, (what has been said on this point)
were you not he who opposed his father in what he
said, not revering him; I quote your poem –

"Sit not content with distress and suffering hunger's
pangs, that people might say he is high-minded and
full of patience;
See for yourself if a land that is not decked out with
plants, is like a land all around hedged in with trees,
rich of growth;
So walk aside from what fools in their sloth are
pointing to, for say, what good can there be in a
bough that never bears fruit?
Lead your beasts from a place where you sustain

much thirst, to pasture-grounds where the fertile flows of rain descend,
And ask the clouds to pour, for if your hands are bedewed, your gain may prosper you."

Then when the Kadi heard that there was such difference in the boy's actions and what he had said, he looked at him wrathfully and said "Fie upon him who belies what he says and changes colour as an evil-spirit changes colour!"

Then the boy said "By Him who has made you a key to the truth, and an opener of justice among mankind, I have been turned rusty since I became thirsty. Moreover, where is the open door and the ready gift? Is there one left who bestows with full hands and when asked for food says 'Eat!' "

Then the Kadi answered him: "Stop, for among the missing arrows is one that hits, and not every lightning deceives, so distinguish between the flashes if you watch the clouds for rain, and only testify of what you know."

Now, when the old man saw that the Kadi was wroth on account of the generous, and thought it a serious thing to reckon all men to be misers, he knew that he would soon show his munificence. So he was not slow in setting his net, and baking his fish before the fire, by quoting quickly:

"O Kadi, you whose wisdom and kindness are more deeply rooted than Mount Razwa,
This youth maintains, misguided by ignorance, that in this world none exercises bounty,
Not knowing that you are the son of a tribe, whose gifts are like quails and manna.
Confer them then that which will make him ashamed of what he forged of impudent falsehood,
And let me go rejoicing and giving praise for the helpful bounty which you will spend on us!"

The Kadi was pleased at this speech, and bestowed on him liberally of his largess, and turned to the boy (for whom he had already shafted the arrows of rebuke) and said: "Have you not now seen the refutation of your assertion, and the error of your opinion? So henceforth do not be hasty in your blame, and pare no wood before testing it; and beware of refusing obedience to your father. If you should continue to revolt against him, you will call down upon yourself from me that which you deserve!"

The youth was silent with remorse, and fell to biting his fingers, seeking shelter by his parent's side. Then, as they went away, the old man recited: "Let him whom his fell fortune has treated ill, repair to Sa'dah town and her Kadi. His bounty shames the bounteous that went before, his justice will baffle those who shall come after!"

Now, I wondered whether I knew that old man or not, and when he set off on his journey I persuaded myself to follow him. I wondered what tree was the fuel of his fire, and I would go with him to his home, if need be, to find out if my suspicions were correct. So I flung from me what clung to me, and set out, and he did not cease to step along and I to follow in his wake, till I was right beside him. Our recognition was mutual, and I was glad to see that he had done away with his shakiness, and when he said "He who deceives his brother may not live long to enjoy life!", I knew that he was the Seruji in very truth and with no change in condition. So I clasped his hand, and inquired after his good and evil hap. He said: "Here is the dutiful son of your brother at hand, ask him what you want to know!" But the boy was laughing too much to speak, and after I had embraced my old friend, I went back to the town, wondering when and where I would find the two of them again.

THE THIRTY-EIGHTH ASSEMBLY

THE ENCOUNTER AT MERV

It had become dear to me, ever since my foot moved and my pen spluttered, to take literary learning for my roadway, and the kindling of my torch for my pursuit thereof. Accordingly, I furrowed out its doctors, and its teachers, and the treasurers of its mysteries; when I had found one of them (such as are the desire of the seeker, and the burning log to light one's fire from) I clutched with my hand at his stirrup, and beseeched him for the dole out of his mind's hoard. I met none that equalled the Seruji in the abundant shower of his clouds, and in applying the pitch to the places where the sympons of scab appear, save that he used to wander abroad swifter than the moon in her changes, and being eager to join in his many peregrinations, I too found great enjoyment in travel. So, at a time when I had strayed to Merv, the rousing of birds, and the presage which is the harbinger of good, gave me happy tidings of a meeting with Abu Zayd, such time as I had I spent spying for him in various caravan parties and any assembly which I saw gathered together. But I found none to tell me where he actually might be at the time of my arrival in Merv, and despair got the better of hope, and expectation became reduced and subdued.

Now, one day I was in the presence of the Wali of Merv, when lo, Abu Zayd rose to sight in the poverty-stricken rags in which he was dressed most of the time, and greeted with the greeting of the needy when he meets the lord of the crown. Then he said to the Wali: "Know you, who may be kept from blame, and spared sorrow, that on him who is entrusted with offices, hope depends, and to him whose degree has been exalted, wants are referred, and that he is fortunate, who, if he has the power and destiny aids him, pays the toll for divine favour, as he pays the toll for cattle, and who clings to the people commanding reverence, as he clings to his wife and close relations. Truly you have become, praise be to Allah, the support of your city, and the pillar of your age, to whose sanctuary the saddle-beasts are driven, and from whose generosity bounties are hoped, to whose courts requests are carried, and from whose palm relief is to be expected, for Allah's grace upon you has been great, and his beneficence on your behalf plentiful. Now, I am an old man who grovels in the dust after having rolled in riches, and who lacks green crops when he has waxed hoary. I have come to you from a distant place, and in a wretched state, hoping from your sea a swell, and from your rank a lift, and hope is the best means of propitiation for him who begs, and the best gift of him who gives. Therefore, please bestow upon me what is incumbent upon you, and deal me fair, as Allah dealt fair with you, and beware that you do not turn your face from him that visits you, and comes to your house. To close your fist from him who asks your gift and appeals for support is not well done, for he excels not who is stingy, nor does he who hoards go the right way. But he is the man of head and heart who, when he has, bestows, and when he first earns a profit, profits others; and the liberal one is he who, when he is asked for the present of gold, is not afraid to give." Then he waited, looking for the fruit of his planting.

Now the Wali wished to know whether his well was shallow, or whether his spring had continuity. So he bent his head to think how to strike fire-sparks from his fire-stick, and how to discriminate the temper of his blade.

But the secret of his silence and of his delay in giving

was hidden from Abu Zayd, so he flared up in the
following words:

"Despise not men of learning because they are clad
in rags of poverty,
Nor fail to pay due regard to him who comes full of
hope, both if he be glib of speech or tongue-tied;
But give your bounty to him who solicits help from
you and raise by timely aid the one whom you see
downcast.
Hail the wealth of a man whose wealth obtains
praise for him,
And he who buys fair renown from humankind by
his gifts, will never be overreached, though he gave
rubies.
But for magnanimity the wise would have no excuse,
if he aspires to what goes on beyond the mere day's
food.
Yet to acquire eulogy he strives, and moved by his
love of nobleness, lifts his neck to aim at high places.
When he who is generous inhales the fragrance of
thanks, he spurns the fragrance of musk, however
finely pounded;
And beneficence is beloved of men for its qualities,
whereas the close-fisted is hated all his days,
And his excuses against spending riches with kindliness, keep blame on him for evermore, and
people's stern censure.
Be bountiful, then, with what your hands have been
gathering, that he who begs for your boon be forever
dumbfounded.
And take your share, before a stroke of fortune
comes upon you that shows your tree of life
deprived of its leaves.
For time is too fickle to endure in one state only —"

Then the Wali called him near on account of his
ravishing discourse, until he had made him many donations, lengthened his skirt for him and shortened his

night. So he rose from the Wali's presence with a full sleeve and a merry heart.

I followed him, keeping in his direction, and tracking his step, until, when he was out of the Wali's gate, I shouted: "May you thrive on what has been given to you, and be allowed to enjoy long that which has been put in your possession!"

Then his face lit up, and he beamed in my direction, and he sent up thanks to Allah (be He exalted), strutting along with a proud swing, reciting:

"Know, who has gained a portion by plodding dullness, or who owes rank to virtues of those before him, that my earnings are due to worth, not to meddling, and my station to power of speech, not to kings' grace."

Then he said; "Out on him who blames learning, and hail to him who strives after it, and makes it his pursuit." And he bade me farewell, and went away, leaving me aflame with longing for more of him.

THE THIRTY-NINTH ASSEMBLY

THE ENCOUNTER AT OMAN

Called by some important business to Oman, on the eastern coast of Arabia, I was soon weary of road travel, and (the Prophet Mohammed once said 'travel is a torment'), I decided to cross the sea in a swift sailing ship.

So I removed my chattels from the camels, and took my water-bags and provisions, and embarked rather trustingly as one who would give himself excuses as to why he would go that way. Scarcely had we settled on board, and hoisted the sails for speed, when we heard from the shore, while the night was darkling and waxing gloomy, a caller who said: "O you people of this strongly-built ship, driven on the high sea by the Mercy of the Mighty, the All-Knowing, shall I direct you to a merchandise that will deliver you from sore torment?"

Then we said "Light for us a brand from your fire, O guide, and show us the right path, as the trusted friend shows the right path to the trusted friend?" He replied: "Will you take for companion a son of the road, who carries his provisions in a basket, and whose shadow is not heavy, wishing for nothing but a sleeping-place?"

So we resolved to lower our wings to him, and not to be stingy in providing for his need. When he had come aboard, he said "I take refuge with Allah from the paths of destruction!" Then he said: "We have been told in the Traditions, handed down by the doctors of divinity, that Allah (be He exalted), has not made it binding on the ignorant to learn, any more than He has made it incumbent on the learned to teach. Now, I possess a charm transmitted from the prophets, and I have sound advice for you, which it is not in my power to conceal, nor in my nature to hide." Then he shouted: "Do you know what it is? It is a good spell for travellers when voyaging on the sea, and the shield against anxiety, when the wave of the deep rages. By it Noah was protected from the flood, together with what was with him of animated beings, as the verses of the Koran record it. I quote: 'Embark ye within, in the name of God be its course, and its riding at anchor!' " Then he sighed, as one who is heavily burdened, saying "Behold, I have stood among you in the stead of a bringer of tidings, and advised you with the advice of the zealous, and have entered you on the path of those who guide aright, so Thou be my witness, O Allah, who art the Best of witnesses." Then his eloquent discourse, conspicuous by its beauty, made us wonder, and our voices were raised to him in recitation. But my heart had from the sound of his voice a tinkling knowledge of the true nature of his sun. So I said to him: "By Him who holds in bondage the bottomless sea, are you not the Seruji?" He replied: "Yes, for how long could the son of brightness remain hidden?" Then I revealed my own self since he had revealed his, and we sailed on, while the sea was smooth, the sky serene, our life pleasant, and our time a sport; and while I was delighted with meeting him again, as the rich delights in his ingot of gold, rejoicing in his conversation, forgot the elements, and suddenly the sea was rushing in on us from every quarter. Therefore we veered, on account of this calamity, towards one of the adjacent islands, to give rest to our ship, and to protect ourselves until the wind calmed down.

The obstacle to enjoying ourselves, however, was that our provisions dwindled to the merest pittance, and we began to fear that we might starve. Then Abu Zayd said to me: "Listen, the gathering of fruit from the tree is not obtained by sitting still and lamenting. Have you a mind to rouse our luck by going inland?" I replied "Yes, I will follow you closer than a shadow, and wait on you more obediently than your shoes."

Accordingly, we two descended from the ship to the island, despite the failing of our strength, to search for provender, though neither of us knew what we might find. After walking quite a while we came upon a lofty castle, with an iron gate, and a troop of slaves in front. These we accosted, and asked them to make a ladder or throw a rope that we might be drawn up, but each of them had so miserable a face, mourning deep in grief, that we asked them what was their sorrow.

They would not answer, and made neither fair nor foul reply. When we saw that their fire was that of the glow-worm and that their state was as that of the mirage of the desert, we said "Out upon you, and may your faces wax unsightly, alas for anyone who hopes anything of you!" Then a servant whom old age had visited, came forth and said: "O sirs, do not increase our pain, for we are in sore anguish, and in an evil plight which makes us disinclined to talk."

Said Abu Zayd "Relieve your choking sorrow, and speak out bravely if you have the power, for you will find I am a competent leech and a healing practitioner."

"Know you that the lord of this castle," said the servant, "is the pole-star of this place, and the Governor of this territory. He was not free from grief because he was childless, until by paying honour to the seed-fields and selecting for his couch the most exquisite partner he was hailed with the noble tidings of the pregnancy of that happy lady, and his palm-tree gave promise of a shoot. Then, when the days and the months were counted, and the time of delivery had come, and the necklace and crownlet for the child were made, the throes of childbirth were so severe that great fear was felt for both root and branch. Therefore, there is not one of us who dares to sleep except in snatches, till we know what will happen." Then he began to weep, and called repeatedly upon Allah to whom we have to return, till Abu Zayd took him by the sleeve and said "Be still, O such a one, and be of good cheer, and receive news of joy and proclaim them, for I possess a spell for speedy childbirth, the fame of which is spread abroad among mankind."

Then his slave hurried to inform his noble master, and before the time which it takes to say "No" sallied out to take us in.

As soon as we had entered the room of the master, he said to Abu Zayd "Your reward will prosper you if what you say is true."

Abu Zayd asked for a reed pen, some meerschaum, and some saffron macerated in pure rose-water. In a breath's time they had brought what he asked for, then he prostrated himself, rubbing his cheeks in the dust, said praise to Allah, whose forgiveness he craved, bidding those present stand, keeping themselves at a distance. Then he took the pen with a mighty extragavant gesture and wrote on the meerschaum with the saffron-solution:

"Child to come, listen to one who warns you beforehand, and yes, warning belongs to faith's foremost duties;

You are safe now within a home closely guarded, an abode from all misery well protected;

None but you sees anything there to frighten you on the part of false friend or foeman frank in his hatred,

But as soon as you come forth from your shelter you alight in a dwelling hurtful and shameful,

Where the hardship awaiting you will soon bring your tears in fast-flowing downpour.

So continue your easeful life and beware of changing things proved with things that are all uncertain,

Being heedful of one who seeks to beguile you, that you be hurled the surer into sorry torment;

Now I have given you, upon my soul, fair advice, but sound advisors are often suspect, and seldom heeded."

The he blotted the writing, and tied the meerschaum up in a piece of silk, and having sprinkled it profusely with ambergris, asked that it be tied to the thigh of the labouring woman. Then, it took no longer than the throat tastes of drinking, or the interval that the milker makes in drawing the milk, before the body of the child slipped out, through the specific quality of the talismanic writing and the might of the One, the Eternal. The castle was immediately filled with joy, and its lord and slaves were ready to fly with delight. They surrounded Abu Zayd, singing his praises and kissing his hands, deeming themselves blessed by touching his tattered garments. Then his revenue continued to come in, from every direction, from the moment the lamb was born until safety was given back to the sea and we prepared for departure. Abundant gifts were poured upon him, and brightened the face of his every wish, and he was vastly content. The governor would not let him depart with us, however, and bade him enrol in his household, so that his hand might be made free with his treasures. When I saw that he was inclined to stay where there were so many riches, I took to rebuking him, and taunting him with forsaking his home and companions. Said he: "Listen to me – Do not cling to a native place where people oppress and hold you in scant esteem; but depart from the land that exalts the low above the high in dignity, and take your flight to a safe retreat, though it were in the lowlands of the Mountains of Kaf.

"Roam about the world at will and where you choose, make there your home, not thinking of your old haunts, nor breathing sighs for distant friends

"For know full well that a free-born man in his own country meets with but scant regard,

"As the pearl is slighted within its shell and underrated in preciousness."

And he continued "Enough then, it should be for you to hear those words which I have spoken; so farewell, make my excuses, to the shipmates."

He then provisioned me, stinting nothing which was in his power to give, and escorted me to the bay, as one escorts one's dearest relative, until I had embarked. When I bade him goodbye, I did so with much grief, lamenting our separation, wishing heartily that the babe and its mother had come to grief, so that he would have been driven from that territory instead of being given such power in it.

THE FORTIETH ASSEMBLY

THE ENCOUNTER AT TEBRIZ

I intended leaving Tebriz at a time when it was irksome for both high and low, being empty of patrons and men of largess. While I was preparing my travelling items I met Abu Zayd, the Seruji, wrapped in a travelling cloak and surrounded by females. I asked him about his business, and where he was bound with his bevy. He said, pointing to a woman, fair of face, but evidently in high dudgeon, "I had married this one, that she might make me forgetful of exile, and cleanse me from the squalor of celibacy, but I met from her no help, in that she now kept me out of my right, now plied me beyond my strength, and through her I am jaded with foot-soreness, an ally to carking care; and here we are on our way to the judge, that he may strike the hand of the oppressor. So, if he arranges matters between us, well and good, if not, then a divorce!" Hoping to be of some use to him, I put my present business behind my back, and accompanied them to the Kadi.

Now, when we got to the presence of the Kadi, who was one of those people who appreciate parsimony, and stint even tooth-picks, Abu Zayd, crouched on his knees before him, said: "Look sir, this my palfrey refuses the bridle, and is much given to bolting, though I am more obedient to her than her fingertips, and fonder of her than her own heart." Then the Kadi addressed her: "Woe betide you, do you not know that stubbornness angers your lord, and requires the lash?"

But she said: "He is one of those that used to prowl behind the house . . ."

"O, out upon you," then said the Kadi to him, "do you sow in the saltmarsh, and look for chicks where no chicks are to be got? May it never go well with you, nor you be safe from terror!"

"By Him that sends down the winds, she is a liar!" cried Abu Zayd.

Said she: "No, by Him who adorned the neck of the ring-dove with a ring, and has given wings to the ostrich, he is a worse liar than I!" But Abu Zayd hissed with the hiss of the flaring fire, and blazed up with the blaze of the enraged: "O you strumpet, woe to you! Slattern! Bane for your husband and for your neighbour, are you resolved in private to torment me and show off in public by giving me the lie? Yet you know, when I made you my wife, and gazed at you, I found you uglier than a monkey, and drier than a strip of hide, and tougher than a palm-fibre, and more offensive than carrion, and more troublesome than the cholera, and more barefaced than the bark of a tree, and colder than a winter's night, and wider than the river Tigris! But I veiled your blemish, and did not disclose your disgrace, though if Shireen the fairest had presented you with her beauty, Zobaydeh (wife of Haroun Al Rashid) with her wealth, the queen of Sheba with her throne, and Rab'iah the sainted with her piety, I would scorn you for my saddle-seat." Then the woman played the tigress, and bared her forearm, and tucked up her skirt, and said to him: "O you mean, cowardly, flighty one, you hurl at me your own shame, and thrust your knife into my honour, while you know you are contemptible, vicious, and more indecent than a fart in company, and more out of place than a bug in a perfume-box!"

Said the Kadi to her: "I see that you are as alike as two old leather bags, or hawk and hunter. So give over, man, the altercation, and enter in on the level road, and as for you, woman, abstain from abusing him, and keep still when he comes to the house by its door."

Then the woman said: "By Allah, I shall not hold my tongue back from him, until he clothes me, nor will I hoist for him my sail, until he gives me enough to eat." Thereupon Abu Zayd swore with three binding oaths that he owned nothing but his tattered rags.

The Kadi looked at them with the eyes of justice, and the sharp-witted, and pondered with the thoughtfulness of the sagacious, then he said to them with a face that he made most stern: "Does it not suffice you, to vilify each other in the judgment hall, and to make bold of this offence, that you needs must proceed from the disgrace of mutual befoulment to the malice of defrauding each other? But I swear by Allah, fundament of either of you has failed the ditch, and your arrow has missed the pit of the throat. For the Prince of the Faithful has appointed me to give judgement between litigants, not to pay the owings of debtors, and by the thanks due to his favour which has established me in this place, and conferred on me the power of binding and loosing, if you do not explain to me further the truth of your case, and the hidden meaning of your deceit I shall surely make an example of you for the benefit of the unwary!"

Abu Zayd looked down before him, as the serpent looks down, and said "Listen, listen: I am the man of Seruj, she is my consort – the full moon has none but the sun for equal. Her company and mine are never severed, I water naught but my own plantation; five nights, it is, however, and mornings, that we have worn the sorry garb of hunger, knowing no more what chewing means, or sipping, so that from sheer exhaustion of our life-breath, we are like corpses new-risen from the graveyard. So, when our patience failed, and every comfort, we came by dint of want, whose touch is painful, to this resort, for good or evil venture, to gain, by hook or crook, some little money. For poverty, when it assails the free-born, leads him to don the shameful cloak of falsehood. This, then, is my condition, and the state of my crops, this my lesson; see my today and ask what was my yesterday, and bid them mend my case or send me to jail at will, for in your hand my weal or woe lies."

Then, the Kadi said to him: "Cheer up and set your heart at rest, for it is possible that your fault may be condoned and donations made plentiful to you."

Thereupon the woman leapt to her feet, and pointing to the people who were present, beckoned to them, saying:

"O folk of Tebriz, you are blessed with a judge who ranks by far ahead of all judges, no fault in him save that his gift on a day of bounty is dealt out in short measure. We came to him that we might cull the fruit from off his tree that never fails yielding; he is sending away the Shaykh rejoiced with his gift, and treated with regard and distinction, but sending me off more disappointed than one who watches for the lightning in August, as though he did not know that it was I who taught the Shaykh to talk with such glibness, and that I could if I wished it make him the laughing-stock of all Tebriz!"

Now, when the Kadi saw the stoutness of both their hearts and the readiness of their tongues, he saw that he was visited through them with an incurable disease, and an overwhelming calamity, and that if he gave to one of the spouses, and turned the other away empty-handed, he would be like one who pays a debt with borrowed money. So he frowned and knitted his brow, and raged and fumed, and hummed and hawed; then he turned about to the right and left, and twisted about in regret and distress, and began to abuse the office of a judge and its troubles, counting up its vicissitudes, reviling those who seek and apply for it. Then he groaned as the despoiled one groans, and wailed abjectly, saying "This indeed is an astounding thing! Am I in one place to be hit by arrows, am I in one case to be made to deal with two debtors, am I to please both litigants?" Then he turned towards his Usher, the carrier-out of his behests, and said "This is not a day of judgement and delivery of sentences, of decision and execution: this is a day of sorrow, this is a day which involves one in debt, this is a day of crisis, a day of loss, this is a day when one is deprived of one's share, not given it. So rid me of these two babblers, and silence their tongues with two pieces of gold. Then, dismiss the company, and close the Court, proclaiming that this is an ill-omened day, and say that the Kadi is in mourning for it, so that no other litigant may come into my presence!"

Accordingly, the Usher said the Amen on the Kadi's prayer, weeping along with him in response to his weeping, and paid out to Abu Zayd and his spouse two *misqals,* and said: "I bear witness that you two are the most crafty among humankind and Jinn, and I would warn you that in future you should respect the courts, and every Kadi is not a Kadi of Tebriz."

So they said to him: "There is not your like among Ushers, and many thanks are due to you," whereupon they got up and stalked away with their two gold pieces, roasting the heart of the Kadi with two fires.

THE FORTY-FIRST ASSEMBLY

THE ENCOUNTER AT TANIS

In the bloom of my youth I responded to the calls of wantonness, and made many a visit to dainty damsels, and listened much to the tunes of songs, until the warner (the gray hair) had arrived, and the freshness of life had turned its back to me. Then I craved for forgiveness, and repented of what I had trespassed in the face of Allah. So I began to drive out evil inclinations by good deeds, and tried to mend my wicked ways before it was too late, and turned from the morning-meeting of the fair and mixing with songstresses to meeting with God-fearing men, drawing near to people of piety. I swore that I would not associate with anyone but him who has rooted out error, and whose dissolute manners had been mended, and when I found one who was ignominious, I fled from him.

When foreign travel had landed me at Tanis, an ancient Egyptian town, at last, the first thing I did was to go to the mosque, to give thanks for my safe arrival. There, I saw a man surrounded by a dense circle of enthralled spectators, and he was saying with a stout heart and clear tongue: "Poor is the son of Adam, aye, how poor! He relies upon the world, on that which is unreliable, and asks from it a stay on that which has no stability, and through his love for it he is slaughtered without a knife. He is addicted to it through his folly, and is rabid after it through his wretchedness; he hoards up in it through his boastfulness, and makes no provision from it for his future state. I swear by Him who has poured out the waters, sweet and salt, and lit up the sun and the moon, exalted the might of the holy stone, if the son of Adam were wise, he would not revel in drinking bouts, and if he thought of what was happening, he would weep tears of blood. He would strive to overtake that which had escaped him, and if he looked at the issue he would better the turpitude of his actions. O, wonder of all wonders, just think of him that plunges towards the abode of fire, while he treasures gold and hoards up riches for his descendants! Again, it is of marvels unheard of that, though the sprinkling of hoary hair warns you, and your sun proclaims its setting, yet you do not see fit to turn and cleanse yourself from your blamefulness."

He paused a while, then continued: "Woe to the man who, warned by his hoariness, still blindly rushes along on youth's folly bent; and glances back on pleasure's fire longingly when all his limbs from weariness shake; who rides the steed of wantonness, which he deems a softer couch than chamberlains ever spread, not awed by silver hair which no man of sense sees coming without its starry light startling him; nor forbidding what right forbids, or hearing anything which may impair fair repute. Aye, such a man, away with him if he die, and if he lives, he's reckoned not alive, there is no good in him; alive he breathes fulsomeness, as though a corpse exhumed ten days after death.

"But hail to him, whose honour sheds sweet fragrance, bright in its spotless beauty, like a broidered gown. So say to him who feels the stinging of the thorn of his sin, pluck out the thorn, poor brother, or you are lost! Wipe out with sincere repentance any writ that black misdeeds have left on your book of deeds, and deal with men of every kind pleasantly, winning with courtly ways both fool and sage; feather the free whose plumage fair time has stripped – may he not live, who, while he can, feathers not.

"Help one oppressed by tyranny; if too weak to help yourself, then summon up hosts for him.

"Raise him who, when he has tripped, calls on you, through him perhaps you will rise on gathering-day; drink this cup of counsel, and bestow on another one who is thirsty what remains in the cup."

Now, when he had concluded this, there was a lad in that assembly who rose to his feet, bare of clothes, and said: "O men of discretion, who listen to injunctions, you have apprehended what has been said, and understood what has been directed; so, whoever of you intends to accept the proffered advice, and to mend his future, let him by benevolence to me manifest his intention. For, by Him who knows all secrets, and condones obduracy in transgression, my hidden state is as you behold me, naked, and my face is well worthy of being spared shame. Do please help me that you may have help conferred on you."

Then the Shaykh said that their hearts should be disposed kindly towards the boy, and many donations were made, so that his empty desert was covered with green very soon.

So when his pouch was full, he hied away with a swagger, singing the praises of the people of Tanis.

After the youth has retreated, the Shaykh decided to stay no longer, and went, after bidding them raise their hands in prayer.

Now, I was on the alert to test him, and to solve this mystery. So I followed while he strode quickly on his homeward way. But when he felt that he was secure from any sudden intruder, he turned his head to me, whom he must have known was following, and greeted me with joy, saying: "Were you pleased with the sharpness of that little fawn?"

Said I: "Yes, by the Guardian."

He said "He is the youngest Seruji, by Him who brings pearls from the deep."

Then I said: "I knew you must be the tree on which that fruit had grown!" And he confessed to the truth of this, and was gratified that I had guessed.

He asked "Have you the time that you could come with me to my house, so that we could pledge each other in the ruddy wine?"

But I demurred: "Woe to you! Will you tell others what to do and forget your own soul?"

He smiled, displaying all his yellow teeth, and said:

"Drive cark and care away with wine unalloyed, and cheer your heart,

Not sinking with fretful grief,

And say of him who blames you for warding off the pangs of pain: 'Enough of you! Begone!'

"As for me," he went on, "I am going where I may quaff my morning and my evening draught, and if you are not willing to come with me and accord with the mirthful, then you are no companion for me, and your road is not my road. So get out of my way, and do not pry or spy after me, turn aside from it." Then, he turned his back on me and went, without casting a glance behind him. I burned with grief at his departure, and stayed behind, heartbroken.

THE FORTY-SECOND ASSEMBLY

THE ENCOUNTER AT NAJRAN

The dicing of travel and the paths of inclination used to throw me about, until I became a son of every soil and a brother of every foreign land, and there was much wagging of tongues because of my journeying.

I was content however, for I crossed no valley, nor witnessed any assembly of divines but I fetched light from the torch of learning that consoles grief, and raises the worth of man. Now, when I had made for a time a stay at Najran, a celebrated town of Yemen, I took its gatherings for my visiting-place and selected there my friends and neighbours. During our meetings I heard both what rejoices the heart and distresses it, being assiduous at them both day and night.

At one of the meetings there crouched before us an old man burdened with senility, who greeted us after the fashion of a beguiler, saying: "O you full moons, seas of bounty, see what you can do to lighten my state. Will you help me or will you recede when called upon?"

They said: "O man, you have angered us so much that, though you intended to open a spring, you might have done so, but have now caused it to sink away."

"You must have been interrupted from some very interesting proposition," said he, "so I beg you to tell me what you were talking about before I appeared."

We were vying with other in proposing riddles, as men vie in shooting arrows in battle, and we told him so.

"Let us riddle together, then," said he, "For you

tongue-gifted ones may be pleased to hear what I have
collected of riddles in my life, and let him be judge who
excels."

We asked him to begin, and he did:

"A maiden I know, brisk and full of speed in her
ministry, returning by the same track as she went by
when starting off;

A driver she has, kinsman of hers, who is urging her,
but while thus speeding her on, is her helpmate too.

In summer she is seen dew-besprinkled and moist
and fresh, but when summer is gone, her body shows
flabby, loose and dry."

As no one could tell what this meant, he explained
that it meant he was talking about the punkah, the
ventilating fan of canvas over our heads.

No sooner had we congratulated him upon that than
he began another: "A son there is of a mother fair,
whose root has sprung from her lofty plant; he hugs
her neck, though for some time she had discarded him;
he who reaps her beauties ascends by means of him
and none forbids or blames." No one being able to
guess this either, the old man told us it was the rope of
palm-fibre which was hidden in that riddle.

Then he said: "Now, here is another for you, O lords
of intellect, fraught with obscurity: One split in his
head is through whom the writ is known, as honoured
recording angels take pride in him; when given to drink
he craves for more, as though athirst, and settles to rest
when thirstiness takes hold of him; and scatters tears
about him when you bid him run, but tears that sparkle
with the brightness of a smile." After we could not
guess who this might be, he told us that he was riddling
upon a reed-pen.

Then he said, "Again this one, O you men of understanding and standards of learning; One restless,
although firmly fixed, bestowing gifts, not working
mischief, now plunging, now uprising again, a marvel
how he sinks and soars. He pours down tears as one

oppressed, yet his fierceness is to be feared: for he can bring destruction on, though his heart be pure." This turned out to be a description of the water-wheel, and in general assent many thought that this was his best, and told the old man so. We begged him to continue, and give us more from his remarkable store.

He obliged with this, placing his traveller's staff under his arm: "One flighty and leaning half to one side, but no man of sense will upbraid him for either; he is always raised up on high as a just king and is rightly exalted for ever in his station. Pebble and golden nugget are alike to him, though truth should in no way be balanced with falsehood, and most to be wondered at in his description, if people regard him with eyes of discernment, is that by his judgement the parties abide, though they know him as flighty by nature and partial."

This caused a good deal of brain-searching, but at last I had to ask the old man for the answer, and he told us that it was a description of the goldsmith's scales.

While we were thus wandering in the vales of fancy, time waxed long and looks grew sad as no one could match him. So when he saw that they rubbed the fire-sticks of thought and no sparks sprang forth, the old man said: "O my good people, have you not enjoyed my riddles, and has not the time come for the hidden to be disclosed, or that the ignorant should surrender?"

So we said "By Allah, you have tried us hard, you have set up the nets and you have caught the game. Give us the price then, for every riddle you have taught us, and we will pay and give you the renown."

Then he fixed for every riddle a fee, and claimed it from us in ready cash. When he was about to leave, the head man of our gathering took him by the arm and said: "Will you not tell us of your pedigree, and tell us who you might be?" He looked sulky, and would not tell at first, so someone said "He is of doubtful birth!" and he spoke these lines at once:

"Seruj is the place where my sun rose, the home of my joy and comfort,

I had to change her for exile, of all my soul took delight in;

No biding-place have I on earth, no rest for my camel,

My morning, my eve pass, one in Nejd, another in Syria,

I drag my life out with food that dejects the heart, vile and abject,

No copper-coin even do I own — a coin? From whom shall I get it?

Who lives a life such as I had, has bought it as a losing bargain!"

Then he put the money he had got into his belt, and went to wander the face of the earth again. We begged him to return, but by my father's life, he did not, and our desire for him never faded.

THE FORTY-THIRD ASSEMBLY

THE ENCOUNTER AT AL-BAKRIYAH

Peregrination that casts a man about, and troublesome travel had wafted me to a tract where the experienced guide would lose his way, and the venturesome be seized with terror, and saw many sights that I loathed, but would not like to talk about. I urged on my jaded beast, travelling as one who throws both divining arrows and then resigns himself to destruction. I trotted and cantered mile after mile until the sun was nearly setting, and light was beginning to veil itself, and fearing the host of Ham (the Father of Blackamoors) I wondered where I might dismount and grope my way. Then there appeared to me the form of a camel in the lee of the mountain, and I made for it cautiously, hoping it would be the riding-beast of someone taking rest. I found I was right, and the animal a swift dromedary, whose rider was lying asleep wrapped tightly in his striped cloak, drowned in sleep.

So I sat down beside his head until he woke, and then when his lamps were lit (his eyes opened), he saw that I was there and started back, saying "Is it my brother or the wolf?" and I reassured him with "One groping in the night, who has lost his way, so give me a light that I might strike it for you."

Then his fear departed, and so did mine, and I became sleepy, and I said "Shall I sleep now?" but he said "No, we should go night-faring," and we saddled our beasts in haste and set out, riding through the whole night, until she had reached her end, and dawn broke, pulling up the tent pegs of night.

I scanned the features of my companion, and it was Abu Zayd, in the morning light, the object of the seeker's delight, and the road-sign of the rightly-guided. We bestowed on each other the greeting of those who have been reunited after a long separation, and intimated our mutual tidings, my camel groaning with fatigue and his flitting along with the fleetness of the young ostrich. I wondered at the strength of her build and the power of her endurance. So I asked him how he had chosen her. He said "Aye, this camel has a sweet story to relate, and pleasant to listen to. So if you would like to hear, let us stop for a while, but if you do not want to, do not listen to it." I assured him that I was all ears, and made my jaded beast kneel down, and made my ear his target.

He began "I bought her at Hadramowt, where I had seen her exhibited for sale, and endured a great deal to acquire her. I took her over lands sharp with stone and flint, and I found her remarkably good for travel, with a ready supply of milk for my provision; no other camel could keep pace with her, and no fatigue ever overcame her. I made her my mainstay for good and evil, and held her in the place of one who benefits and gives joy. Now, it happened that she strayed some little while ago, and I had no other mount. So I was over-whelmed with grief, and well-nigh undone, forgetting every calamity that had gone before, and remaining three days without being able to travel on, and without tasting sleep, except a little at a time. Then I began to follow up the roads and search the pastures, and the halting-stages, but I got no sign of her, and whenever I remembered her fleetness and her readiness to vie with the birds, the thought of her loss near crazed me. One day when I was in the tent-village of some clan, I heard a distant person and some isolated voice crying out 'Who has lost a mount hailing from Hadramowt, one easy of step, her bridle is plaited and her back is one that has been broken and reset. Weariness does not

come near her, she needs no stick, she furthers the
journey at the oncoming of night, and she has no
blemish.'

"I was drawn towards the caller and said 'Give me
the mount, and take what you ask for her.' 'What is
your mount like, describe her,' said the man who had
found her, 'May your error be forgiven you!' 'A camel
whose body is like a hillock, her hump like a dome, her
milk the fill of a pail, and I would have been given
twenty dinars for her, when I alighted at Yarbin.' Then
he turned from me, and said 'You are not the owner of
my trove.' Enraged, I took hold of his collar, and persisted, and tried to tear his garments, while he said 'O
such and such a one, my mount is not the one for
which you seek, so withold from your rashness, and
stop your abuse, or take me before the judge of this
tribe, who is not liable to error, and if he gives her to
you, take her, but if he does not, go and jabber no
more.'

"Then I saw no cure to my anxiety but to go to the
judge, so we hastened to a Shaykh with a handsome
headgear, stoutly erect, whom one could perceive was
not unjust.

"Thereupon I broke forth complaining of ill-use and
lamenting, while my companion was silent, until, when
I had finished, he brought forth his sandal, heavy of
weight, made in Hadramowt, and said '*This* is the
mount I described, not a camel! This stranger must be
an opportunist, one who seeks something which he
does not own.'

"Then the judge took the sandal, and looked at it,
and said 'This is my sandal, which I had lost, and as
for the mount you have described, it is in my dwelling.'

"I was so relieved, that I gave thanks to Allah, and
said 'I swear it by the ancient house, the worshipful,
and those that circumambulate the holy frame, you are
a good man to appeal to for justice, the best of Kadis
judging amongst Arab tribes, so live as long as camels
speed the pilgrims on!'

"Then he replied without deliberation, and on the spur of the moment 'Allah reward you for your thanks, dear nephew, though I expect no thanks as ever due to me; for the worst of men is he who wrongs, when made a judge, and who, when made trustee of ought, betrays his trust.'

"Then he ordered one into my presence, who then went and brought my camel to me, and I went away trailing the skirts of joy, calling out 'How marvellous!' "

Then I said to Abu Zayd, "You have told a wonderful tale indeed, have you ever found one more gifted in the sorcery of the tongue than yourself? A finer craftsman in fashioning the jewellery of speech?"

He replied "By Allah, yes, listen and enjoy what you will hear. I had intended, at one time, to take a wife, at a time when I made for Tihameh, so that she might be a helpmate to me. Now when the resident proxy for the conduct of the marriage negotiation had been instructed, and the affair was all but concluded, I sallied forth in the morning like one who seeks a stray beast, and was early with the earliness of the diviner from the flight of birds.

"Then I encountered a youth, whose face pleaded in his favour, and as he had such a cheering aspect I decided that I would take light from his views on matrimony.

"Said he 'Do you wish her to be a matron, or a maid that gives trouble?' I replied 'Choose for me what you think fit, I have put the matter in your hands.'

"Then he said: 'To me then belongs the explanation, and on you devolves the application, so listen, may I be your ransom, after the burial of your enemies! As for the choice of a virgin as a wife: she is a treasured pearl, a hidden egg, early fruit ripening for gathering, a fresh meadow, one that must agree with you, a necklace costly and precious, none has soiled her with his touch, no deflowerer has despoiled her, and no wanton has plied her. She has a face suffused with shame, and a bashful eye, her tongue is faltering and her heart is pure, she is a playful puppet and a sportive doll; she is a frolicsome gazelle, with accomplished gracefulness, a jewelled belt bright and new, and a sharer of your couch that rejuvenates, not ages. But for the matron – listen – she is the trained steed, the ready morsel, the desire made easy, one who has gained knowledge by repeated practice, the fond companion and confidental friend, the skilful and well-advised, the intelligent and the experienced. She is the hasty meal of the rider, a slip-knot for the suing suitor, an easy mount for the enfeebled, booty swiftly snatched by the combatant. Her disposition is gentle, her bonds are light to bear, her inward state is clearly manifest, and her service adorns; I swear by Allah that I have been observant and truthful in both descriptions, and I have thoroughly displayed the two kinds: by which is your heart enraptured?'

"Then," said Aby Zayd, "I said 'I have heard that a virgin is stronger in her love, and less given to wiles.'

"Said he 'Upon my life, this has been said indeed, but how many a say has not been true? Woe betide you, she is a filly refusing the bridle, and the mount difficult to be tamed, the fire-shaft reluctant to be struck from, and the fortress hard to conquer. Moreover, the provision she requires is plentiful, and the help she affords is scanty, her enjoyment is savourless, and her coquettishness is provoking, her hand clumsy, her temper a snake that will not be charmed, and her disposition forward; her night is a long and dark night, and to break her in is a heavy task; to know her needs the lifting of a screen, and often she puts the combatant to shame, and is averse to being sportive, and angers one inclined to play, and humbles the experienced stallion. Also, it is she who says "I dress and sit in company, so I seek one who holds and spends." '

"Said I to him, 'What do you think of the matron, then, O father of all that is sweet?'

"Said he: 'Woe betide you! Listen – do you hanker for the remnant of the meal, the residue of the watering-ponds? For draggled garments and worn-out vessels, for one who has browsed on every pasture? One lavish of expenditure, grasping and never satisfied? And all her talk is "I was and have now become, before when I was wrong I had help given to me, but what a difference between today and yesterday, and where is the moon beside the sun?" Do you hanker for her that is always bewailing her former husband, blessed with bold grown-up sons, and herself a wanton? She is a collar round a man's neck, she is an ulcer that never heals.'

"Then I said to the youth: 'Shall I become a monk then, and enter *that* path of conduct?'

"He replied: 'Woe to you, will you enter upon the path of monks, when their plight has been made manifest? Fie on you and them! Fie on the weakness of your understanding! You show yourself up when you pretend that there is monkery in Islam; as if you had not been told of the wedlock of our Prophet, may purest peace be upon him! Or do you not know that a good helpmate puts your house in order, obeys your voice, sobers your sight, and brings your fame into good odour? Through her you behold the coolness of your eye and the flower sweet to the nostrils, and the joy of your heart, and the lastingness of your memory, and the solace of the day and the morrow (offspring), and how are you averse to the ordinance of the sent ones, and the enjoyment of the wedded, and the path of the guarded, and that which draws forth wealth and sons? By Allah, you should think on these things.' So I said to him 'Will you strut away from me so jauntily and leave me bewildered like this?' 'I suspect that you pretend goodness and indulge yourself a bit, so that you may dispense with a damsel exacting a large dowry!' he said, then, with a smile.

"Said I 'Allah confound your suspicions, and not allow your generation to grow old!' Then I went away from him, and repented of consulting striplings."

I, myself, looking at Abu Zayd, was sure that he had never met such a youth, and had merely contrived to tell me this delightful story by inventing him.

"Abu Zayd," said I, "I swear by Him who has planted the forests that this controversy was carried on by you and yourself!" So he burst out laughing and said "Lick up the honey and ask no questions."

Then I began to expatiate in the praise of learning, and to exalt its owner above the possessor of riches. But he glanced at me and winked at me indulgently, and when I persisted in my thesis, he said: "Hush, hear from me and inwardly digest:

"They say that a man's chief adornment and pride, his beauty is learning deep-rooted, sound,
Alas, it adorns but the wealthy and him whose summit of lordship is rising aloft;
But as for the poor man I reckon for him far better than learning, a loaf and a stew.
What beauty bestows it on him, if they say a scholar, a school-drudge, or maybe a clerk."

And when he had finished, and I was digesting it, he continued: "Presently there will come evidence to you which will show you the truth of my assertion, and the full illustration of my argument."

So we travelled on with unfailing strength, and without flagging, until we came to a village (may the good keep aloof from it!) to seek fresh provisions, for we were both short of provender.

Now we had not reached the halting place, and the spot assigned for the kneeling of the camels, when a lad came to us with a bundle of grass on his shoulder. Abu Zayd greeted him with the salutation of the Moslem, and asked him to give him some information. "What do you wish to ask?" said the boy, "May Allah prosper you!"

"Are there any fresh dates for sale here?" asked Abu Zayd, and the boy answered "No, by Allah."

"Any green dates?"

"No, by Allah!"

"Nor fruit for night-talk?"

"Far from it, by Allah!"

"No bread in exchange for choice verses?"

"Be silent, may Allah preserve you!"

"Honey-fritters for poems?"

"Nay, not so!"

"Sifted flour for subtle sayings?"

"May Allah restore your senses!" responded the boy, "May Allah guide you aright!"

But Abu Zayd took pleasure in reiterating question and reply, measured out from this self-same sack, and the youth thought that the Shaykh must be a devil. So he said "Let this suffice you, and be satisfied with what I am telling you – in this place poetry does not fetch a barley-corn, nor prose a crumb, nor narrative a nail-paring, nor a treatise slop-water, nor the history of battles a morsel of meat, for among these people here there is not one who will give a gift of any sort, or reward when a poem has been fashioned for him, none who shows himself bountiful when a tale has diverted him, none who provides support, and with them the learned are like waste springs. If no rain falls in abundance, it has no value, and no beast approaches it; and in a like manner, learning, if no wealth abets it, its study is a weary toil, and its profit nothing." Whereupon he departed. Abu Zayd said to me: "Are you aware now, that learning is slack, and its one time helpers have turned their backs on it?" I admitted the sharpness of his sagacity, and resigned myself to the decree of necessity.

Said he: "Let us leave off using words, and do what we can to get some food. Will you give me something to sell here?" I handed him my sword, which was the best thing I had to dispose of, and he, promising to get what he could for it, rode off and out of my sight.

I stayed a long time waiting for him, then I got myself up on my mount to follow him, but I was like one whose milk has run short in summer, for I met neither him nor my sword in any part of that place.

THE FORTY-FOURTH ASSEMBLY

THE ENCOUNTER CALLED 'THE WINTRY'

This Assembly contains a series of puzzling statements, made by Abu Zayd in a circle of guests, who on a cold winter night warm themselves at the fire and enjoy the profuse hospitality of a generous entertainer. The intelligibleness of these statements, like that of the legal questions of the thirty-second Assembly, depends on the double meaning of the terms in which they are worded. Apparently, therefore, they refuse translation into any other language, which cannot supply similar ambiguities, but it must not be forgotten that the more recondite meanings of the several idioms require explanation even to the average Arab, who is not initiated in all the subtleties of his mother-tongue, and notably in this particular instance the English reader, who consults the short notes, attached to each puzzle, has even the advantage over Abu Zayd's audience. For the wily Shaykh amuses himself by secretly departing in the middle of the night, without vouchsafing to his fellow-guests the interpretation promised for the morning, and probably thinking that his noble and presumably highly cultured host does not need it. He who has made himself acquainted with the hidden meanings, and then once more peruses the *double-entendres* in their entirety, can scarcely fail to be vastly delighted by the string of seeming absurdities and contradictions, which, moreover, in the Arab original forms a poetical composition with the same rhyme running through the whole. While adhering as much as possible to the metre, the translator had, as in all other poetical passages of the work, to renounce this adornment, and be contented with occasional alliterations and assonances.

I came in a night of deepest darkness, black of locks, upon a fire kindled on a mountain-top, and giving tidings of liberality, and it was a night whose sky was cold, her bosom closely buttoned, veiled her stars and

her misty gloom heaped up. I was colder in it than the
eye of the chameleon, and a mangy goat, so I urged on
my sturdy camel, saying "Hail to thee and my own
soul!" until the kindler [of the fire] spied my person
and became aware of my speedy faring, when he came
down in hot haste, and indited in the *rejez* metre:
  "Long life to thee, groping along thy nightly way,
  whom sheen of fire has shown, nay, brought him as
  a gift,
    To one of ample bounty and of vast abode, who
  welcomes, as the miser welcomes golden coin,
    Nightfarers seeking hospitable fare and who
  evades not visitors with 'not at home',   ·
    No tardy one to entertain in friendly guise a guest,
  when all the ground is bound with wintry cold,
    And storm-portending stars are stingy with their
  rain. Well is he wont to ward against the ills of time:
    He gather ashes, sharpens knives, and never fails,
  be it in daytime or at night, at morn or eve,
    To slaughter well-fed camels, and to kindle fire."
Then he accosted me with the countenance of the
bashful and clasped my hands with the clasp of the
generous, and led me into a house whose camels
roared, whose cauldrons boiled, whose slave-girls
carried provisions, whose trays went round, and along
the sides thereof were guests dragged hither by him
who had dragged me, and moulded in my mould, who
were culling the fruit of winter and rejoicing with the
glee of those endowed with youthful vigour. So I joined
the place where they warmed themselves, and found
with them the pleasure which the inebriated finds in
wine; and when embarrassment had passed away and
the cold was gone, trays were brought to us like lunar
halos in roundness, and like gardens adorned with
flowers which were laden with the victuals of festive
banquets, and well fenced against [the fault-finding or
cavil of] the blamer and caviller. Then we spurned
what is said about gluttony, and saw sense in plunging

into it, until, when we had meted to ourselves with the measure of the greedy and come nigh the risk of indigestion, we had handed to us napkins to wipe off the odour of food, whereupon we settled in the seats of night-talk and every one of us began to wag his tongue and to display what he had in his show-case, except an old man whose side-locks were hoary, both whose upper garments were tattered, for he crouched apart and kept far aloof from us. So his reserve, the motive for which was incomprehensible, and which would have excused anyone who censured him, angered us, save that we softened our speech to him and were afraid to encroach on him by questioning, and each time we wished him to overflow as we overflowed, and to launch out in what we launched out, he turned aside as the lofty turns aside from the lowly and quoted: "Verily this is nought but idle tales of the ancients" (Koran, vi. 25, and *passim*). Presently it was as though shame had smote him, and the forbidding soul had whispered to him, for he crept up and came nigh, putting away his fastidiousness and exerting himself to make amends for what had gone before. Then he begged a hearing from the night-talkers, and broke forth like the coursing torrent, saying:

"Marvels I know, seen by me, and told without any lie, for not in vain am I called the father of wonderment:

Folks have I seen, O my folk, that on a crone's juice are fed; not, notice well, mean I though the daughter of grapes by her.

(*baula 'l-'ajuz,* lit. *urina anus,* is a popular idiom for "cow's milk"; *al-'ajuz,* old woman, means also "choice old wine".)

And Arabs, at famine's time, who relished as dainty food, a roasted rag, and allayed indeed therewith hunger's pangs;

(*khirqah,* a tatter, a rag, and also a swarm of locusts.)

And powerful men I saw, who said when things went amiss, or when they did carelessly their work: 'It was fuel's fault';

>　(*qadir,* who is able, strong, powerful, and also "who cooks food in the kettle", *qidr,* when it is called *qadir.*)

And scribes whose hands never wrote a letter in all their lives, and who read not any more aught of what is writ in books;

>　(*katib,* one who writes, a clerk, a scribe, and also "a cobbler, a mender of water-bags", etc.)

And people who in their flight in eagle's wake sped along, although they were heavily arrayed in helmet and steel;

>　(*uqab,* a black eagle, and also "a standard": Mohammed's standard was called *al-'uqab.*)

And gathered folks, men of worth, to whom appeared suddenly a noble dame and they turned away, to flee far from her;

>　(*nabilah,* a lady of distinction, and also "carrion", whence the phrase *tanabbala 'l-ba'ir,* the camel became putrid, *i.e.,* died.)

And eke a troop, who for sure have never seen Mecca's fane and yet had made pilgrimage on camel's back without doubt;

>　(*hajjat jusiyan,* they performed the pilgrimage sitting crosswise [on their camels], and also "they got the better in argument in that posture", *jusiy,* being the plural of *jasi,* one who sits crosswise.)

And women-folk faring from Aleppo all through the night who came to Kazimah-town at morn without weariness.

>　(*sabbahna kazimat-an,* they reached in the morning Kazimah, a town in the dependency of Basra, and also "they wished good-morning to a woman silent with anger".)

And people from Kazimah who faring forth during

night found themselves in Aleppo about the time morning dawned.

> (*asbahu fi halab,* they arrived in the morning in Aleppo [far distant from the former town], and also "they passed the morning in milking".)

A youth I saw who for sure had never touched lady fair, and yet he had progeny to keep alive name and race.

> (*naslun min al 'aqib,* progeny of surviving children, and "also an enemy at his heels".)

Again one hoary not hiding ever his hoariness, who in the desert appeared still young of years, far from grey.

> (*sha'ibun ghaira mukhfin li 'l-mashib,* one hoary who conceals not the hoariness, and also "one who mixes milk [with water] and makes no secret of the milk thus mixed".)

One suckled with mother-milk, not lisping yet with his lips, I saw him in hot dispute amidst a brawl loud and fierce.

> (*fi shijarin baina 's-sabab,* in contention between arguments or revilings, and also "in an [open] camel-litter between the cords"; to the latter meaning of *sabab* Hariri quotes Koran, xxii. 15: "let him stretch a cord to heaven".)

And one who sowed millet stone, and when it came to be cut, it turned, forsooth, jujube shrub, which merry men dearly love.

> (*al-ghubaira,* an intoxicating liquor prepared from millet, also called *sakrakah,* of which a tradition says: " 'beware of the ghubaira', it is the wine of the world", and also the Arabic name of the plant *Zizypha rubra Gilanensis.*)

And one who was bound and rode upon a horse also bound, but never ceased all the while to fare along amblingly.

> (*maghlul,* put in chains, fettered, bound, and

ghulla, he was bound, have also the meaning
"thirsty", and "he was suffering from thirst".)
And one I saw, free of hand, who led a fine saddle-
beast, in haste, although captive and a brother of
misery.

> *(ma'sur,* one taken captive, made prisoner of war,
> and also "one suffering from strangury.")

One sitting, while walking, and with whom his beast
fell aground, though strange it seem what I tell, yet it
admits naught of doubt.

> *(jalis,* one who is seated, and also "one who
> makes for Najd"; *mashi,* a pedestrian, and also
> "owner of cattle," in which latter sense some com-
> mentators explain *imshu,* in Koran, lxvii. 15, as a
> prayer in behalf of mankind for abundance of
> cattle and prosperity.)

A weaver too, both his hands cut off, I saw, deaf and
dumb, if this you deem marvellous, well, wonders
will never cease.

> *(haik,* a weaver, and also "one who in walking
> moves his shoulders, and keeps his feet far
> apart.")

One straight of build met I once, whose stature rose
like a lance, on Mina mount, who complained to me
of back-crookedness.

> *(al-hadab,* being hump-backed, and also "rough
> rising ground".)

One who exerted himself in giving all creatures joy,
yet cheering them thought a sin like lying or
tyranny.

> *(ifrah,* rendering cheerful, and also "burdening
> with debts," as in the saying of Mohammed:
> "There is none left in Islam burdened with debt
> [*mufrah*] whose debt has not been paid.")

And one who loved people to commune with him
secretly, but never had any need for converse with
humankind.

> *(hadisu 'l-khalq,* conversation with created

beings, and also "the telling of a lie," as in Koran
passim: "this is but a lying tale of the ancients.")
One scrupulous who redeemed always his word
faithfully, lacked none the less conscience according
to Arab ways.

> *(zimam'* conscientiousness, and also pl. of
> *zimmah,* "a well with scanty water," when the
> words translated "according to Arab ways"
> would have to be taken in the sense of "on the
> road of the Arabs," meaning in the desert.)

One full of strength, never was there yieldingness
seen in him, his softness was manifest withal, and
quite unconcealed.

> *(lin,* softness, smoothness, yieldingness, and also
> "a palm-tree or plantation," whence Koran, lix. 5:
> "your cutting down some of their palm-trees.")

And one prostrating himself on camel's back,
unconcerned at what he did, thinking it an act of
prime piety.

> *(fahl,* a vigorous camel-stallion, and also "a mat
> made of the leaves of a male palm-tree" *[fuhhal].)*

One who excuses, and pains him whose excuse he
accepts, though coaxingly, while in screams is he
who thus is excused.

> *(azir,* one who accepts another man's excuses, and
> also a "circumciser"; *ma'zur,* one excused, and also
> "a boy being circumcised.")

A town I saw, waterless for him who would scoop a
draught, though water flows over it with torrent's
rush many times.

> *(baldah,* a city town, district, and also "the space
> between the eyebrows," which is also called
> *buljah.)*

A village too, less in size than any nest built by
birds, in which there lived Dailamites on plunder and
robbery.

> *(garyah,* a village, and also an ant-hill; *dailam,*
> name of a people in Gilan and extended to non-

Arabs in general, and also "a swarm of ants";
khulsatu's-salab, sudden robbery, and also "bark
of a tree.")

A star I saw, when it shows, a man is no longer seen,
as though a veil covered him, a veil that naught
penetrates.

(*kaukab,* a star, and also "a white speck in the eye
producing blindness"; *insan,* man, and also metaphorically "the pupil of the eye.")

A ball of dung, highly prized as part of one's
property, the owner though recks it not by any
means much of wealth.

(*rausah,* the excrement of any hoofed animal, and
also "the tip of the nose.")

A platter of purest gold, I saw it bought after much
hard bargaining for a grain, a solitary silver grain.

(*nuzar,* pure gold, and also "wood of the *na'b*
tree," of which trays, cups, bows, and similar
objects are made.)

One gathering poppy-seed to ward from him off the
foes assailing him, and he was not disappointed
therein.

(*khashkhas,* the plant called *abu 'n-naum,* father
of sleep, *i.e.,* poppy, and also a troop of armed
and armoured men.)

And oftentimes passed me by a dog in whose mouth
there was a bull, but know ye, it was a bull without
any tail.

(*saur,* a bullock, a bull, and also "a piece of soft
cheese.")

How many an elephant, I swear it, has seen my eye
on camel's back, perched upon a saddle and saddle-
bags.

(*fil,* an elephant, and also "a man of weak
intellect, a dolt".)

How many a man I met complaining in desert-
tracts, and no complaint uttered he in earnest or
pleasantry.

(mushtaki, one who complains, and also "one who uses the small water-bag", called *shakwah).*

A pitcher I saw again, a shepherd's girl in the wold was owning it, and it looked with twain of eyes bright as stars.

(karraz, a pitcher with a narrow neck [the Qamus reads the word in this meaning *kurraz*], and also "a he-goat on whose horns a herdsman carries his utensils.")

How often times saw my eye two springs the water whereof, though in Aleppo they were, was flowing from farthest West.

(al-gharb, the distant West, applied to Maghrib or West Africa, and also "the lachrymal gland"; *'ain,* a fountain, source, spring, and also "the eye.")

And one who pierces with spears, although his hands never held a lance, and he never leaped against a foe charging him.

(qana, pl. of *qanat,* a lance, a spear, and also "an aquiline nose," applied to which *sada'bi-hi* means "he disclosed or uncovered it.")

How many times came I to a land without any palms, and on the morrow I saw dates newly grown in their sheaths,

(busr, dates beginning to ripen, and also "rain-water lately fallen"; *qulub,* pl. of *qalb,* pith of the palm-tree, and also of *qalib,* "a well.")

How often a spacious tray in desert tracts have I seen, that in the air was on wing and swooping down from on high.

(tabaq, a large tray, and also "a swarm of locusts.")

How many old men I saw that lived in this world for aye, and who, I ask you, escaped destruction at any time?

(mukhallid, one who lasts eternally, and also "one whose hoariness is slow to come.")

How many wild beasts I met complaining of hunger's pangs with fluent speech and a tongue more piercing than cutting swords.

(walsh, a dumb brute, a wild beast, and also "a famished man.")

How often one who had eased his bowels called me and talked to me, and nor he nor I in manner were lacking aught.

(mustanji, one who cleans himself after evacuation, and also one who sits on a elevated place [*najwah*].)

How oft I made kneel my beast beneath a pomegranate-bud that would have shaded no end of 'Ajam [*i.e.,* foreign] and Arab men.

(junbuzah, the flower or bud of a pomegranate, a bud in general, and also "a dome, a cupola"; *'urub,* here probably by poetical license for *'urb,* Arabs, may also be taken as pl. of *'arub,* "a woman fond of her husband," as in Koran, lvi. 36: "loving their spouses, of equal age with them.")

How oft I saw one rejoiced a little while, and his tears were seen to fall freely as the drops of rain from a cloud.

(surra, he was filled with joy, and also "his navel-string was cut," the remaining part being called *surrah,* navel.)

How often times have I seen a shirt that hurt badly him who owned it maiming his limbs, unnerving him thoroughly.

(qamis, a shirt or vest, and also "a beast given to jumping and rearing.")

How many a veil there is, if time but would make away with it, I trow numerous wayfarers would stay at home.

(izar, a wrapper or veil covering the upper part of the body, and also used metaphorically for "woman.")

So far, and how many more of wondrous arts owns my mind, and sallies of pleasing wit, and sayings choice, sweet to hear.

So if you are quick to seize the drift of words, you will find that all is true and my bloom leads you to guess at my fruit.

But if you are baffled, then the fault, forsooth, lies with him who knows not how to discern 'twixt sandal and common wood."

Then we began to grapple with his verse, and the explanation of the riddles proposed by him, while he made game of us as the careless makes game of the perplexed, saying: "It is not thy nest, so get thee gone!" until the birth proved too difficult and the debarment complete. Therefore we thrust the lead on him, and asked him for enlightenment, and we were suspended between hope and despair, he saying: "The coaxing before the call for milking." So we knew him to be one of those who want to return to their gift, and expect a bribe for their judgment.

Now it galled him who had given us shelter, that we should be exposed to a mulct, or ignominiously frustrated; accordingly the lord of the mansion sent for a camel of the breed of 'Id, and a robe like Sa'id's, and said to him: "Take them both as a lawful property, and levy not from my guests [even] a trifle for a forfeit." Said he: "I testify that this is a disposition like Akhzam's and liberality like Hatim's." Thereupon he approached us with a countenance whose serenity was translucent and whose brightness beaming, and said: "O my people, the night is well-nigh gone, and drowsiness has got the victory, so betake yourselves to the sleeping-places, and snatch the repose of the sleeper, so that ye may sip a draught of refreshing rest and rise invigorated, when ye will understand that which is explained to you, and things difficult will become easy." Then every one approved of his opinion, and laid himself down on the pillow of his slumber. Now when the lids were closed in sleep and the guests had fallen a-doze, he sprang to the camel, and straightway saddled her; then he mounted her and started her on the journey, saying, addressing her:

"Seruj, my camel, is thy goal, so fare apace, now through the night, now through the day, now day and night,

So that thy hoofs may gladly tread her pastures moist and thou mayst find thee thence well off and prosperous,

And safe of being jaded over hill and dale: ay haste thee on, my precious beast, and speed they pace,

Crossing the flinty mountains, peak by peak, contented with a chance draught from the wat'ring pond,

And not alighting until yonder goal is reached; for I have sworn it, and in earnest made my oath

By worship due to Mecca's lofty-pillared house, if thou but bring me safely to my native town

Thou wilt for aye be held by me instead of child."

Then I knew that it was the Seruji, who when he had sold out, was wont to start off, and when he had filled his bushel, to decamp, and as soon as the dawn of the morrow broke and the sleepers recovered from their sleep, I informed them that at the time when unconsciousness had overcome them, the Shaykh had given them the slip for good, and mounted his camel and departed. Then a fresh vexation took hold of them after vexations of old, and they forgot the good of him for his bad. Thereupon we disbanded in all directions, and went away under every star of heaven.

THE FORTY-FIFTH ASSEMBLY

THE ENCOUNTER AT RAMLAH

I had gathered from men of experience that travel is a mirror of marvels, wherefore I began to cross every desert and brave every danger, in order that I should experience everything wonderful. Now, one of the strangest adventures I reckoned pleasant was when I was in the presence of the Kadi of Ramlah. He was one of the finest of the lords of power and wealth I had ever met. One day there appealed to him an old man in very worn raiment, and a fair one in extremely faded finery.

The old man was minded to speak first, but the lady cut him short, and checked him, inditing with the tongue of an impudent shrew (once she had removed from her face the flap of her kerchief):

"O Kadi of Ramlah, in whose hands there is for us the date or else the cinder-hot coal,
To you I complain of my mate's cruelty, who pays his pilgrim duty to me but once in a while;
Would that, when his devotion has come to an end, and he has ceased his pebble-throwing,
That he would go and join the lesser upon the chief pilgrimage;
This is his way in spite of the fact that I have never crossed him in anything,
So bid him show me in future more sweet kindness, or make him taste the bitter draught of divorce,
Before he puts from him the last shred of shame."

Then the kadi said to the old man: "You have heard what she lays at your door, that you do not do your duty by her in the way you should. So turn aside from

that which disgraces you, and beware of angering her
and coming to grief."

Thereupon the Shaykh crouched on his knees before
the Kadi and uttered these lines:

"Listen, you whom no blame may reach, to the
speech of one who clears himself of the doubts cast
on him;

By Allah, not from hatred do I turn from her, nor
has my heart's love for my spouse died away,

But fortune's fitful freak has come over us, ruthlessly
robbing us of both pearl and bead,

So my abode is empty, as her neck is unadorned by
shell or gold ornament.

And since fortune fell I left dolls alone, like one who
vows chastity for caution's sake,

And not from grudge did I hold aloof from my fields
of pasture,

Only from fear to see the seed spring in harm, and
children come to starve –

So blame not one who in such a plight finds himself,
rather be kind to him and hear his word."

Then the woman flared up and unsheathed arguments to fight him, saying: "Woe betide you, fool, you
lack-food and lack-lance, do you make so much fuss
about a child coming, when Allah has given to every
grazing creature a grazing-ground? Your understanding has surely strayed, and your arrow missed its aim;
you are a wretch, and your wife is wretched through
you!"

The Kadi pronounced: "He is truthful in pleading
his poverty, there is enough in his concern for his
rumbling entrails to make him forget his pendulum."

She dropped her head, looking askance, and made
him no reply, so either shame had come to her or
victory encompassed her. The Shaykh said to her "Out
on you, if you have concealed anything which is known
to you." She said: "Alas, is there any concealment
after appeal, and is there a seal remaining upon any

secret? Would that we had been visited by dumbness, and not repaired to the judge!" Then she covered herself with her kerchief, and pretended to weep at her exposure.

The Kadi began to wonder about them, and to admire their form of address, and blamed fortune on their behalf, feeling new sympathy in his heart for them. He brought out two thousand dirhems, saying "Take these, and resist the mischief-maker between two friends." So they thanked him profusely, and departed as united as if they were wine and water.

After they had gone, the Kadi began to praise their cultured minds, and asked "Is there anyone here who knows them?" Then the foremost of his henchmen said "As for the Shaykh, he is the Seruji, to whose excellence all the world witnesses, and as for the woman, she is his travelling consort, but as for their litigation, it is a wile of his device, and one of their hunting-nets."

The Kadi of Ramlah was angered at what he heard, and burned with rage to see how he was cheated. He said to the informer: "Get up and look for the pair of them, and bring me news of what they did after leaving here!" So the man rose, and went off, but after a long while returned, defeated.

The Kadi said "Let us know what has happened; and do not conceal from us any vileness which you have found out about them both." He replied: "I followed in their wake, and overcame all obstructions, finding them at last in a desert place. I told them that they should return here to give account of themselves, but both were divided as to whether they should return. "The return is praiseworthier," said she, "I think to flee is cowardly!"

"No," said the Shaykh, "yours is the most foolish notion.

"Take my advice, and follow its guarded way, and let the sun suffice you for details;

Fly from the date-tree when you have had your pick, and separate for good from it afterwards,

Beware of returning to it even though its keeper made it free to all comers,

For best a thief should not be seen in a spot where he has given proof of its cunning.

Then he said to me: "You have taken trouble in coming after us, so return and say to him who has sent you 'Gently, let your bounty not be followed by injury Or else your wealth and fame alike will be gone.

And do not fly into a passion because a beggar exaggerates,

For he is by no means first to polish and gloss his speech.' "

The Kadi cried out at this: "Allah confound him! How charming are his ways, and how exquisite are his arts!" Then he sent off his spy with two mantles and a purse full of gold coin, saying "Go speedily like one who turns neither to right nor left, until you see the Shaykh and his consort, and moisten their hands with this gift, and show them how eager I am to be beguiled by the learned!"

THE FORTY-SIXTH ASSEMBLY

THE ENCOUNTER AT ALEPPO

An overpowering longing and a most ardent desire carried me to Aleppo, and at that time my back was light and I was quick. I took travelling gear and sped there with the flight of a bird, and ever since I had put up there, I whiled away my days in all that satisfies. At last my heart had no longer power to addict itself to anything, and the raven of separation took wing after his alighting.

Then my mind, free of care, and sweet wilfulness, urged me to make for Hims (Emessa), so as to pass the summer in her territory, and to sound the proverbial stupidity of the people of her soil.

So I hastened towards her with the swiftness of the shooting star, when it falls to stone the listening devils, Allah avert them from our path. Now, when I had pitched my tent on her boundary, and found the fragrance of her breeze, my eye spied a Shaykh whose old age was coming on and whose youth had turned its back on him. Around him were ten youngsters of one root and diverse roots, and I approached him that I might probe in him the learned folk of Hims.

Thereupon he met me with a cheerful face and greeted me with an even handsomer greeting than I had given him. Then I sat down to test the fruit of his speech, and to fathom the essence of his clownishness. He pointed with his staff at the oldest of his chicks, and said to him: "Tell us some couplets, and beware of keeping us waiting." So the boy crouched as the lion crouches and said:

"Make ready for your envier's sharp weapons, but
deal kindly with him who sets up hope in you;
Cut yourself off from play, avoid wantonness, but
ply the camels and the brown supple spears,
Strive to obtain a lofty place, pillared high, not to
enrobe yourself in gay dalliance,
For lordship means, by Allah, not quaffing wine, nor
gain you glory courting girls of full hips.
Hail to one free of hand and mind, large of heart,
whose only joy is giving joy to the good,
His water-pond is sweet to those seeking it, nor
waste his wealth when one in hope begs for it,
Expectant hope is not refused at his door, and not
put off; he deems delaying hope vile.
He does not follow the course of loose sportiveness,
nor is the wine-cup ever seen in his hand,
Stern discipline and self-reproach make him rule
over his heart and master his lust and greed,
And he wins praise through knowing that one-eyed
wives are not endowed with that possessed by wives
with sight."

The Shaykh then said to the boy "You have done
well, O you little full-moon, O you head of the
fraternity!" Then he said to the next who seemed to be
a brother of the former: "Come near, my little
luminary, O Nuwairah, my moonlet, display the bridal
couplets, even though they are not of the choicest."

The boy took his reed pen in hand, nibbled it, and
wrote:
"Fair Tajanni has maddened me and bewitched me
with her thousands of wily tricks and beguilings,
Has enamoured me with her eyelid's droop, like a
doe's, draining mine of tears through her love-
charm.
She approached me, adorned and richly attired, and
crazed my senses with forms that gleam through her
movements;
Then I fancied she favoured me and would soothe

me by her speech, but an idle dream proved my
fancy.
After using with me her heart's cruel lie, like one
faithless, who would appease rightful anger,
She forsook me, and let me go, softly weeping, and
in sorrow that ceaselessly bred sorrow."
When the Shaykh looked at what the boy had
devised, and scanned attentively that which he had
written, he said to him: "A blessing has been bestowed
on you among the fawns, as there has been a blessing
on that olive-tree. Now, you come out, my Qutrub, my
little fidget, and put this into mongrel couplets, and
avoid blunders." There came forward a boy who was
like the star of a dark night, an ivory figurine, and he
took the reed-pen and wrote:
"Be bountiful, bounty is a jewel, and disanoint
none who hopes for shelter;
Do not refuse him who asks assistance, be he rude in
his asking, or modest;
And think not that time will leave for ever the miser
to starve upon his riches; be lenient; do not condemn
men of worth.
Expand their hearts with the joy of giving;
Betray no trustworthy friend, and crave not for coin
that, when tested, proves false."
The Shaykh said "May your hands never wither nor
your knives get blunted!" Then he called out: "O
Ghashamsham, you Essence of the perfume of
Mausham!" Out came a lad like the pearl of the diver, to
whom he said "Write down something, and may no
mishap befall you!"
The boy took from him the pen and penned without
stopping:
"Zaynab's stature, erect and lithe, kills beholders,
and her bosom is a bane to lovers,
Her neck and her grace are helping hosts to her, and
languid eyes that dart glances of deadly sharpness,
Proudly bearing herself she swayed in full-blown

power, now my foe, now with glowing cheeks
drawing near to me,
In the morning or the night, to leave me again in sore
distress at the cruelty of her doings,
Then she came, may I be her ransom, and cooed,
and with her greetings appeased her love-lorn and
beloved one."

The Shaykh scanned carefully the lines the boy had
set down, and his glance ran over it, finding the writing
beautiful and the punctuation correct. "May your ten
fingers never dry up!" he said. Then he called a lad of
bewitching looks, and said to him "Recite two couplets
that will silence every speaker."

The boy answered, "Listen, and may your hearing
never become hard, nor your senses scattered!"

"Make thee a mark, whose traces show fair to sight,
give thanks for gifts, though trifling as sesame-seed,
And shun deceitfulness with all might and main, that
thou mayst gain thee lordship and weight with men."

The Shaykh cried out: "You have excelled, O imp, of
Father of Despoilment!" Then he said: "You have all
done well, my sons may your mouth never be harmed,
nor he benefited who speaks harshly to you. Now, I have
made you all drink from my pure draught, and have
straightened you as spearshafts are straightened, so
think of me and I will think of you, and give me thanks,
and I will not be ungrateful."

I looked at the Shaykh, blinking as one who tries to
see in the dark, and when he found my bewilderment
evident, he smiled at me, saying:

"If Hims I have chosen, and trade as a buffoon, it
was to be blessed with the portion fool-borne,
For our age selects only the fool for its favours, and
houses its wealth in the pools of the hollows,
While brothers of wisdom obtain from their age not
more than does the donkey tied up in the courtyard."

Then he added "If teaching is the most honourable
of crafts, and the most profitable of merchandises, the

most successful of intercessions, the most excellent of eminences, and its possessor is lord of a rule obeyed, and of awe widespread, and of a flock of subjects submissive to his sway, he guards with the guardianship of a prince, and fixes allowances as a Wazir fixes them. He ordains with the authority of the powerful, and resembles the owner of a great kingdom, save that in a short while he reaches his dotage and becomes famed far and wide for foolishness, and shifts about with small wits in his dealings, and none can enlighten you better in this matter than one who speaks from experience."

I said to him: "By Allah, you are the son of the days and pattern of the patterns, and the wizard who beguiles understandings, who has access to every branch of speech."

Thereupon I never ceased to attend his assemblies, and plunged into the current of his river, until the bright days passed away and grey events took their stead, and I separated from him with tears in my eyes.

THE FORTY-SEVENTH ASSEMBLY

THE ENCOUNTER AT HAJR

I needed a cupping, and accordingly (while I was staying in Hajr al-Yemaneh) sent to a Shaykh who cupped skilfully.

I sent my slave-boy to summon the wise man, but he was slow to return after he had gone, and I began to fear that he had met with an accident, or run away.

Then he came back like one who had failed in his errand, and disappointed his master. I said to him "Woe betide you, for your tardiness, and failing to give a spark from your fire-shaft."

Then the boy told me that the Shaykh was as busy as a woman with two butter-bags in the middle of a battle. Now I was loath to go to a cupper's place, and I was at a loss about whether to go or to stay behind and wait for him. At last I decided to go, and when I reached his place, I saw an old man of clean aspect, surrounded by ring after ring of onlookers, and throng upon throng of customers, talking loudly to them.

Before him stood a youth straight as a sharp sword, about to be cupped, and the old man was saying "I see that you have stretched out your head, before you bring out your money, and show me your neck as if to say 'This is for you'. I am not one of those who sell ready goods before being paid, nor look for the shadow after the substance. So if you will dole out your coin, you will be cupped in both your neck-veins, but if you believe in stinting, and hoarding becomes you more, then read the Sura 'He frowned and turned away' and vanish from my sight – or else – ." Then the youth said

"By Him who has forbidden the forging of lies, as He has forbidden the chase in the two sacred precincts, I am more penniless than a babe two days old, so grant me a delay until times have got better for me."

The Shaykh said to him: "Fair promises are like the shoots of a tree, that has an equal chance that it perish, or that fresh dates may be gathered from it. So what will that teach me, whether I am to reap fruit from your tree, or to derive from it an ailment? Furthermore, what relying is there, when you have got yourself far away, that you will fulfil what you have promised? For in reality, treachery has become as white horses' forefeet among the adornments of this generation! So rid me, by Allah, of your presence, and go where the wolf howls in the wilderness!"

Then the lad said: "By Allah, one who breaks faith is cursed, and none do it but the mean, the contemptible, and none resorts to the pond of treachery but the worthless, and if you knew who I am, you would not speak to me this way, but you have spoken in ignorance, and where you should have prostrated yourself, you have behaved foully, and how beautiful are these words I will now repeat to you: 'The stranger who trails his skirt pompously meets with scorn, how will he fare abroad when meat and drink fail him? But no distress brings disgrace on the high-minded man; camphor and musk, as you well know, spread fragrance through being pounded. The ruby is often tried in the fire's fiercest glow, the fire abates but the ruby will remain ruby still'."

Then the Shaykh said to him: "O you bane of your father, who cause your kinsmen to wail, are you in a place to brag of, and of an account to be blazed forth? And granted that your house be that which you claim, do not hammer cold iron, and boast of your belongings (when you do boast) but not the root from which you spring, and of your own qualities and not of rotten bones, and of your valuables, not your pedigree. Do not yield to your ambition, or it will bring you to a fall, nor follow your lust lest it lead you astray. I commend to Allah him who said to his son: 'Be upright, my dear son, for the straight tree will spread its roots, whereas, when it grows crookedly it will speedily pine away.'

"Do not obey debasing greed, but behave as a man who bears in silence the pangs of hunger that gnaw at his vitals;

And battle against lust that destroys you, for many who had soared to the skies, fell, enslaved by lust, and came to grief.

Be helpful to your kinsfolk, for it is shameful to see the pinch of distress in those depending upon the free.

And keep to the friend who when the times turn their back on you, does not betray you, but proves faithful, no matter what goes wrong with you;

And pardon, if you are strong, for there is no good in a man who needlessly wounds, when power of wounding is in his grasp.

And guard you from complaining; you hear no man of sense complain, but the fool, who snarls and growls when he checks himself."

Then the lad said to the onlookers: "How wonderful! What a strange rarity! Nose in the sky and rump in the water! Words as sweet as wine and deeds as flinty as stone! You are indeed a fashioner of fine speeches, who swerves from the road of kindliness. You preach benevolence yet act with the ruthlessness of the cat. If the briskness of your trade is the cause of your crustiness, then may Allah strike it with slackness and allow it to be spoiled by enviers, until you are seen bereft of customers, and your livelihood narrower than the eye of the needle, Inshallah!"

The Shaykh said to him: "No, may Allah visit you with blisters all over you, and heated blood, until you are driven to a cupper of mighty roughness, heavy in charges, with blunt cupping-knives, and breaking wind at every moment."

Now, when the youth saw that he was complaining to one that would not be silenced, intent on opening a door that should be kept locked, he stopped bandying words with him, and made ready to depart. But the Shaykh knew that he deserved blame for what he had said to the youth, so he felt inclined to pacify him. He then vouchsafed to cup him, and not to ask a fee at all, but the lad would not hear of it, trying to flee from his presence. The old man began to beseech him to stay, and pulled at his sleeves, until he tore them in his anxiety. Then he cried aloud at his great loss, both of his honour and the tearing of his rags, with the Shaykh trying still to placate him.

"May I be your ransom!" exclaimed the Shaykh, "let that which grieves you pass over! But will you stop wailing, can you not learn forbearance? Have you not heard of him who exercised forgiveness, taking after the speech of him who said: 'Quench by your mercy the fire of anger that recklessly a churl has kindled in you, and pardon his trespass; for mercy is by far the best of jewels that grace the wise, and the sweetest fruit culled by man is ready forgiveness'."

Then the youth said to him "If you were to know my sordid life, you would understand my tears. But the smooth-skinned make light of what the back-sore feels." Then, as he had now stopped crying, and seemed to have recovered himself, he said to the Shaykh: "I have conformed with your wish, so patch up what you have torn."

The Shaykh said: "Get you gone, you overtax the flow of my bounty; spy for another's lightning, not mine." Then he rose to go from row to row, and begged gifts of the standers-by, inditing as he was wending his way through them:

"I swear by Mecca's holy house, whither the pilgrims flock from far and wide,

If I possessed but food for one day, my hand would
never touch the lancet or the cupping-cup; nor
would my soul, that craves for fair fame with men,
Contentedly put up with this sign of trade,
Nor had this youth complained of harshness from
me or felt the lacerating prick of my sting,
But alack-a-day, foul fortune's fell fitfulness, left me
to grope my way in pitch-black night
And poverty brought me to such a pass; the blazing
pit of hell I would prefer!
Is there a man then whom compassion impels, and
tender feelings prompt to prove kind to me?"
I was the first to commiserate with his misfortune,
and doled out to him two dirhems, saying within
myself, "They are not much to lose, even if he be a
liar."

So he rejoiced at the first fruit of his gathering, and
the dirhems continued to pour in on him, and came
from all sides, until he had a large bagful of coins. He
seemed to be cheered at this, and congratulated himself
on the event, saying to the youth with the torn sleeves:
"This is a half-share for you, take it and do not be
abashed." They divided the money between them with
great care, and rising to go, he found me in his path.

"My blood is heated," I said, "and I beg you to cup
me, that I might obtain relief." He looked at me, and
scanning me sharply, said, in his inimitable style:
"What do you think of my cunning and beguiling,
and what happened between myself and my kid
yonder?
That I come off as victor in the contest, and feed on
fertile meadows after famine?
Tell me, my heart's core, tell me, pray, by Allah,
have you ever set eyes on one such as I?
To open by my sleight of hand each padlock, to captivate all minds by witchcraft? To blend serious with
sportive humour?
If Alexander had been before me, the dew precedes

the shower, but the shower excels the dew in bounty."

His poetry made me realize that it was our Shaykh, Abu Zayd, to whom every finger points. So I rebuked him for lowering himself, and for that self-abasement. But he took no notice, and did not mind what I said, saying "Any shoe suits the barefooted who has to tread on flints."

With that parting shot he walked away contemptuously, and started off, he and his son, like two race-horses and were soon out of my sight.

THE FORTY-EIGHTH ASSEMBLY

THE ENCOUNTER AT HARMAMIYEH

(Told in the words of Abu Zayd himself)

I had not stopped since I bestrode my stout camel (leaving behind wife and children) to catch a sight of Basrah, with the craving of the oppressed, since the possessors of knowledge and the lords of tradition agreed upon the eminence of that city's schools and scholars, the glories of her tombs and martyrs, and I begged Allah to let me tread her soil, that I might wander there.

Now when good luck had landed me there and my glances pastured in her freely, I saw all that fills the heart with delight and makes every stranger forget his native land. So I set out one morning when the taint of darkness was vanishing, and my sauntering brought me to a quarter known as sacred and named after the Benu Haram. It was full of much-visited mosques, of tanks of fine water frequented a great deal, and buildings of solid structure and mansions of pleasing aspect.

"My heart's desire of holy things and worldly which you find there, and neighbours of motley character,
One all wrapped up in scripture's wondrous verses, the other thrilled by tunes of the trembling lute-string;
One skilled in solving deeply hidden meanings, the other bent on loosing the bonds of captivity;

How many there, who wear out their eyes by reading, or wear out their trays by feeding the needy stranger,
How many places of resort for learning, and seats of bounty, lavishing sweets of harvest,
And mansions where from morn to evening there warble peerless maidenly minstrels.
So join, if so inclined, this one in prayer, or if you will, that one in broaching wine-casks,
For there without restraint you may indulge in the wise man's converse or the debaucher's tankard."

Now, while I was scouting her thoroughfares and gazing at her fairness, I saw a mosque, about the time of sundown, renowned for its beauties, and deriving splendour from its frequenters, where the people were running a race in the course of debate. So I turned towards them, in order to ask rain from their cloud. Then suddenly the voices rose for the prayer-call, followed by the coming forward of the Imam, when the blades of speech were sheathed, and the people stood up, so that devotions diverted us from asking for food, and worship from seeking bounty.

But when the due of obligatory prayer was discharged, and the congregation dispersing, there emerged from the crowd an elderly man of sweet eloquence, who possessed an easy flow of speech and great fecundity. Said he: "O Neighbours, whom I have chosen before the branches of my own tree, and whose precincts I have made the house of my refuge, whom I have taken for my kith and kin, and made my stay for the time of my presence, know that the vestment of truth is brighter than costly garments, and that ignominy in this world is lighter to bear than ignominy in the world to come, that religion is the imparting of sincere advice, and guidance the indication of a sound faith; that the consulted has a claim to confidence, and that the seeker of the right direction has a claim to be counselled, that he proves to be your brother, not he who finds excuses for you. Your friend indeed is he who tells you the truth, not he who says 'True' to all you say!"

Those who were present said: "O you our loving friend, and cherished intimate, what is the secret of your riddling speech, and what is the explanation of your concise address? For by Him who has bestowed your affection upon us, and has made us the sincerest of friends, we shall not withhold from you our advice, nor be sparing in our gift."

Then he replied: "May you be rewarded with good and preserved from harm, for you are of those of whom a companion need not complain, and from whom dissimulation does not come, in whom no expectation is disappointed, and from whom no secret is concealed. So I will disclose to you what rankles in my breast, and consult you on the matter that exhausts my patience. Know then, that, while my fire-shaft yielded no spark and good luck kept aloof from me, I was sincere in my purpose of covenant with Allah, and pledged my vow to Him, that I would never buy wine or associate with drinking-companions, nor quaff strong drink, nor don the garb of inebriety. But my misleading lust and my abasing and deluding sensuality prompted me to keep company with mighty drinkers, and to pass round the cups, to put away gravity and suckle myself with grape-wine, and to be forgetful of repentance, as we are forgetful of the dead.

"Nor was I content with this once, but I was addicted to the old vintage even on the fifth day and allowed myself to be thrown prostrate by the bright wine during the sacred night. Therefore see me, contrite for my abandoning the way of return to God, and exceedingly penitent for my indulgence in constant drink, greatly in fear from the breach of my covenant and openly con-

fessing my excess in quaffing the formenting must. Is
there an atonement you know of, friends of mine, To
bring me far from sin, and near to my Lord again?"

Now, when he had finished this discourse, and
satisfied his need of complaint about his distress, my
soul whispered to me "Abu Zayd, this is an opportunity for catching game, so tuck up your sleeves from
your arm and sinew and go to work." Whereupon I
rose from my roosting place, as the alert one rises, and
went forth from my position in the row of worshippers,
saying:

> "You, distinguished by noble rank, great in glory
> and princeliness,
> Who desires a guiding hand to the path of eternal
> bliss,
> I am able to cure the ill, that deprives you of
> peaceful sleep;
> Listen then to a wondrous case, fraught with
> perplexity for me.
> Once I had in Seruj my home, seat of faith and right-
> eousness, where obedience was paid to me for my
> wealth and my lordly state.
> Throngs of guests were resorting to my abode and
> received my boon,
> For I purchased praise with my presents, and kept my
> honour by bounty bright,
> Caring nothing that my treasures went in profuse
> liberality,
> And I kindled the fire above, which the miser is fain
> to quench,
> That the strayer might find with me hoped-for
> shelter and resting-place,
> None thirsting watched my lightning's flash and
> remained still a prey to thirst;
> Many came to borrow my fire-shaft's light and it
> never failed to flame,
> While the times were still in league with me I spread
> round prosperity.

Till the Lord wrought a change in what through His
favour had been my wont,
For He settled the Greeks in our country after a feud
that rose
And they seized on the households of all believers
in one true God
And deprived me of all my goods either hidden or
free to view.
Thus I became outcast in distant lands and a
fugitive,
Who beseeches men's bounty as it had once been
sought of me,
And such misery is my lot, that it makes me wish for
death;
For the height of calamity, which has robbed me of
all my cheer,
Is my daughter's captivity, who was captured for
ransom's sake.
Cast a glance then, upon my woe, and stretch out
your hand to help me,
Ay, protect me from fell fortune, that has wronged
and been my foe,
Aiding me to redeem my child from the hostile
degrading bond.
By such acts are the sins wiped out of a servant who
has rebelled,
As repentance is accepted from one renouncing all
worldliness,
And they are an atonement for him who, though
guided, has swerved astray.
Though I speak this in strains of verse yet my speech
leads aright and true;
So accept the advice I give, and my guidance with
thankful heart,
and bestow what may be at hand, winning praise
from my gratitude."

Now, when I had finished my long and rapid improvisation, and he whose help I implored was satisfied with the truth of my words, his eagerness instigated him to display generosity in my assistance, and he took the trouble to relieve my distress. So he dealt out to me a ready dole forthwith, and was profuse in ample promise of more, so I returned to my nest gleeful at the success of my stratagem.

Then Harith, son of Hamman, said to me: "Praise be to Him who has created you, how mighty is your trickery and how low your inventions!" But I burst out laughing and without hesitation recited:

"Live by deceit, for we live in times whose sons resemble the forest lions.

Set aflow the rills of wile so that the mill of life may briskly turn around;

Hunt for eagles, and if the chase should fail, content yourself with a tuft of feathers.

Try to cull the fruit, but if the fruit escapes you, be satisfied with the leaves;

And ease your heart from distracting thoughts at the frowns of fickle and adverse fortune,

For the ceaseless change of vicissitudes proclaims the doom of our life's unstableness."

THE FORTY-NINTH ASSEMBLY

THE ENCOUNTER AT SASAN

The report came to me that Abu Zayd had reached the age of ninety-three (called the grip of death, or the clenched fist), and the fetter of old age had robbed him of the power of rising. So he sent for his son, after having collected his thoughts, and said to him: "O son, behold the time for departing from the threshold and for having my eyes anointed with the kohl-pencil of demise has drawn near, and you, praise be to Allah, are my heir-apparent. You are the leader of the flock of Sasan after me, and you will be called upon to exhort men's minds, and be a furbisher of their thoughts. Preserve my bequest, and eschew disobedience to me. Pattern yourself upon my ways, and ponder upon my saws, for if you be guided by my counsel, and take light from my morning, your alighting-place will be rich in herbs and the smoke of your fires will rise aloft in the sign of hospitality. If you make light of my advice, your people and kin will make light of you. O my son, I have tested the true state of things, and experienced the vicissitudes of fortune, and have seen a man held worth his wealth, not his pedigree, and inquiry is made about his gain, not his deserts. Now I have heard that the means of livelihood are ministry and commerce, and husbandry and handicraft. So I have plied these four to see which of them is the most fitting and profitable. But I have not proved living by them praiseworthy, nor found ease of life plentiful in them, for the opportunities of rulership and the perquisites of administrations are like the entanglements of dreams. They are like shadows vanishing with the darkness, and a sufficient anguish for you is the bitterness of being weaned from them. And as for the goods of trade, they are subject to risks, and a butt to depredatory inroads, and they are like to swift-winged birds. As for the undertaking of farms and applying oneself to tilling the ground, it is a source of demeanment and a drag impeding advancement, and rarely is its pursuer exempt from despisal or blest with tranquillity of mind. And lastly, as for the crafts of artisans, they do not yield more than the merest pittance, and do not sell briskly at all times, and most of them are dependent on the prime of life. I see nothing easy to win, sweet to taste, and in its acquirement pure of nature, but the craft of which Sasan has planted the roots and diversified the branches, whose light he has made to shine in the East and West, and whose beacon he has kindled to the poor, the sons of dust.

"So I engaged in its battles, sporting its badge, and chose its mark as my ornament, since it is never slack merchandise, and the spring of water which never sinks, and the lamp to which all come and by which the blind and the one-eyed obtain light. And those who exercise it are the most powerful of all tribes, and the luckiest of people, no touch of oppression overtakes them, no drawing of the sword harasses them, they do not fear the sting of biting vermin, nor do they submit to any, either near or far. They are not in awe of him who lightens or thunders, nor care for him who in his fretful anger rises up and then sits down again. Their assemblies are pleasant, their hearts at ease, their food is sped before them, and their times pass brightly. Wheresoever they alight, they pick up, and where they slip in, they strip; they make no country their home and fear no king; and they do not differ from the birds that are hungry in the morning and full at eventide."

Then his son said to him: "O my father, you have spoken true, in what you have said. But explain to me how I may gather in a harvest, and from which end the shoulder of mutton is to be eaten."

Said he: "O my son, bestirring oneself is the door to it, and alacrity is its array, and sharpness of wit is its lamp, and pertness is its weapon. Be more on the move than the wolf that plays the tiger, travel swifter than the locust, be quicker than the gazelle by moonlight, rub the fire-staff of your fortune by your own effort, and knock at the door of your sustenance by your own activity. Cross every mountain-pass and dive into every deep, forage over every pasture-ground, and sink your bucket into every fountain; do not weary of begging, and be not chary of exertion, for it is written on the staff of our elder Sasan; 'He gets who begs, he who roves makes sure of his loaves.' But beware of sloth, for it is a presage of calamities and the garb of the indigent, the key of poverty and the germ of affliction, the token of folly and weakness, and the habit of the helpless, the dependent. He gathers no honey who has chosen laziness, nor does he fill his palm who thinks ease is a smooth bed. So step boldly forward, though it be against the lion, for daringness of the soul gives speech to the tongue and freedom of motion to the rein, and by it eminence is reached, and affluence obtained, even as cowardice is the twin of sluggishness, and the cause of failure, a hindrance to action, a disappointment to hope. Therefore it is said in the proverb: 'One who dares, fares well, he who fears, will fail!'

"Sally forth then, my son, with the earliness of the raven, and the boldness of the lion, and the prudence of the chameleon, and the cunning of the wolf, and the greed of the pig, and the nimbleness of the gazelle, and the craftiness of the fox, and the patience of the camel, and the blandishments of the cat, and the diversity of the colours of the humming-bird.

"Beguile by the gliding of your tongue and deceive by the sorcery of your eloquence; inquire after the state of a market before bringing your goods to it; ask the travellers before visiting a pasture-ground, coax the teat before milking, make the ground smooth to your side before lying down. Sharpen your sight for taking omens from birds, and train your perception for drawing inferences, for he who is right in reading character will have the laugh for a long time, while the prey of him who guesses wrong will be tardy. Make, my son, your burden light, be averse to a repeated draught and content it with a drizzle instead of a downpour. Extol the value of the paltry and be thankful for a trifle, do not be disheartened at a refusal, nor deem it far from possible that the rock should ooze, and do not despair of the mercy of Allah, for none despair of the mercy of Allah but the faithless. And if you have to choose between a mite ready at hand and a pearl promised to you, incline to the ready, and prefer the day that is to the morrow that is to be. Delay leads to loss, and intentions are subject to change, and promises are prone to be postponed, and between them and their fulfilment lie mountains, ay, what mountains! Display the patience of men of purpose, and the forbearance of the considerate, shun the harshness of one who exceeds bounds, and assume the habit of a cheerful disposition. Keep tight the strings of your purse, blend lavishness with parsimony, nor open it to its full extent. When a country disagrees with you, or a trouble has befallen you there, cut off your hope from it, and speed away from it with your camel, for the best of countries is that which betters your state. Do not think departure burdensome, nor hate removal, for the chiefs of our sect and the elders of our tribe have agreed that motion is a blessing and changes of place like a promissory note, whereas they blame him who holds that peregrination is a bore and migration an infliction, and they say that it is an excuse of those who are contented with a paltry pittance and gratified with poor fruit and bad measure. But if you have resolved

on journeying abroad, and get ready for it your wallet
and staff, make choice of a helpful companion, before
you set out.

"There, my son, is a bequest for you, such as none
before was ever bequeathed yet,

One bright and fraught with the essence of choice
rules and maxims that guide aright,

Selected as a counseller sincere and earnest in his
advice,

So act according to what I teach, as a wise and well-
conducted one,

That admiring people will say 'This in truth is
yonder's lion's whelp!' "

Said he "O my son, I have given you my last behest,
and made it right complete. Now, if you follow it, well
done, but if you do not, out upon you! And may Allah
be my substitute with you, and I trust you will not belie
what I think of you."

Then his son said to him "O my father, may your
throne never be brought low, nor your bier uplifted.
You have indeed spoken true, and taught right, and
bestowed on me what father never yet has bestowed on
a son; and if I be spared after you (but may I never
taste your loss!), I will mould my manners on yours,
the excellent, and follow your traces, the illustrious, so
that it may be said how like is the night to yesterday,
and the morning cloud to the cloud of evening."

Then Abu Zayd rejoiced at the answer, and smiled
and said: "He who resembles his father does not wrong
his mother's fair name."

It has come to my knowledge that when the sons of
Sasan heard these beautiful mandates, they prized
them above all others, and learned them by heart, so
they reckon that these are the best things they can
teach their children, and more profitable to them than a
gift of gold.

THE FIFTIETH ASSEMBLY

THE ENCOUNTER AT BASRA

I was wrapped up in sadness one day, whose brunt was fierce, and as I had heard that resorting to assemblies of invocation removes all veils from men's minds, I saw that for putting out the live coal within me nothing but making for the mosque at Basra would do. Those chairs were well-filled, those fountains were frequented, so that the flowers of speech might be culled in its meads, and the whirring of pens was to be heard in its precincts, so I sped thither without delay and without swerving. When I set foot on its gravel and got sight of its uttermost end, I espied a man in worn-out tatters upon an elevated stone, round whom throngs of uncounted numbers were clustered. Therefore I hastened in his direction, and sought access to him, hoping to find the cure of my disease, and I shifted places, surviving knocks and blows, until I was seated opposite him, and lo! it was our Shaykh of Shaykhs, Abu Zayd the Seruji, nor did anything disguise him.

Then at his sight my grief subsided, and the hosts of my cares were scattered. But when he saw me sitting, he glanced at me, and began: "O you people of Basra! May Allah keep and guard you, and strengthen your piety. How far spread is the fragrance of your fame, and how surpassing are the virtues that distinguish you; your country is the most eminent of countries in purity, the richest of them in natural gifts, the widest in expanse, and the most fertile in pasture-grounds; she boasts over others the most correct kiblah, the broadest stream, the greatest number of rivers and date-palms, the most exquisite beauty in detail and aggregate, being the gateway to the sacred land, and fronting the door of the Ka'beh, and the station of Abraham, one of the two wings of the world, (the other is Kufa) and a city founded on fear of Allah, that never was defiled by flames of the fire, whose people never circumambulated idols, and prostrated themselves on her ground to none but the Merciful; possessed of shrines much visited and mosques thronged with worshippers, of schools far celebrated, and of tombs resorted to by pilgrims, of monuments revered and enclosed precincts.

"In it meet the ships and the saddle-beasts, the fish and the lizards, the camel-driver and the sailor, the hunter and the tiller, the harpooner and the lancer, the shepherd and the swimmer, and to it belongs the spectacle of the tide that rises and the tide that ebbs. But as for you, you are of those whose excellences are not to be contested, no enemy gainsays them. Your community are the most obedient lieges to their lord, and the most grateful for benefits bestowed on them. Your ascetic is the most devout of mankind, and the brightest light on the road of truth. Your scholar the most learned of all ages, and the supreme authority for all times, and from amongst you he came forth who created and laid down the lore of grammar, and he who devised the measures of poetry, and there is no boast of man, but to you belongs the foremost hand in it, and the winning arrow.

There is no glory, but you are the most worthy of it, and the most deserving. You have more muezzins than the people of any other town, and in worship you observe the rules, and from your pattern is taken the ceremonies of others, and in the month which is sacred, when the sleepers are sound asleep, there is heard among you a recitation that rouses the somnolent, and rejoices the wakeful, and the smile of morning does not dawn, but the prayer-call summons you with a murmur, like the murmur of the wind on the sea-waves. The Tradition has disclosed that your murmur in the mornings would be like the murmur of bees in the desert. Honour then to you and hail to your city, though it be effaced and nothing remain of it but an outline!"

Then he checked his tongue and put an end to his speech, and their eyes fell on him, and taunted him with falling short, but he sighed the sigh of him that the lion's claw has clutched, or of him that is dragged to execution, and said: "As for you, O people of Basra, there is none among you but is worthy of renown alike for learning and liberality; but as for me, he who knows me – well I am such, and the worst of acquaintances is he who injures you; but to one who does not know me, I will now disclose my character. It is I, who have fared to Nejd and Tilhameh, to Yemen and Syria, in the desert and the sea, in deepest night and early morning. In Seruj I was reared, and in the saddle I got my training. I have entered straits, and opened roads that were closed, and witnessed frays, and soothed tempers, and curbed the restive and closed nostrils in the dust, and melted the frozen, and softened rocks. Ask me of the East and the West, the hoofs of camels and their humps, assemblies and hosts, tribes and squadrons, and gather clear tidings of me from the reporters of traditions and the story-tellers at night-talks, from the drivers of caravans, and the sharp-sighted diviners, that you may know how many mountain-passes I have threaded and veils I have rent. How many perils I have braved, and how many fights have I fought, how often have I beguiled the minds of men, and devised novelties and snatched opportunities and made lions my prey; how many a high-flown one have I left prone, how many a hidden one have I brought out by my spells, how many a flint have I ground until it split, and made spring its sweet water by my wiles.

"But there has passed what there has passed, while the bough was fresh and the temple raven-haired, and the raiment of youth was still new; whereas now the skin has withered, the straight grown crooked, the dark waxed light, and nothing remains but repentance, if it avail, and to patch up the rent that has widened. Now, I had been apprised by reports well supported, and by traditions authenticated, that on every day a glance from Allah, be He exalted, falls upon you, and whereas all men's weapons are of iron, your weapons consist of prayer and the profession of one God. So I repaired to you, jading my saddle-beasts, and travelling from station to station, until I stood in this place before you, though thereby no obligation be laid upon you, since I did not speed here except for my own need, and did not toil but for my own tranquillity, and I do not crave your gifts, but beg for your prayers, nor do I ask for your wealth, but solicit your supplication. Pray then to Allah, may He be exalted, to accord me grace for repentance and readiness for my return to Him, for He is the most High in dignity and answers prayers, and He it is who accepts penitence from His servants and forgives transgressions.

"Allah's forgiveness I crave for sins that, woe is me,
I have wantonly committed,
How often have I plunged into seas of error, and
morn and eve walked in paths of folly.
How often have I followed passion's prompting,
been arrogant, greedy and deceitful,
How often have I spurned the curb in rushing
headlong and unchecked to fell rebellion,
How often have I reached the bounds of trespass,
and never ceased from careering onwards,
Would that I had been forgotten, and never gathered
what, alas, I gathered;
Far better death to him who sins, than to pursue
such a course as I sped!
But O my Lord, grant to me forgiveness; Your

Mercy is greater than my trespass."

Forthwith the congregation commenced to aid him with their prayers, while he turned his face heavenwards, until his eyelids brimmed with tears and his agitation became conspicuous, while he cried out "Allah is greatest! The sign of acceptance has appeared, and the veil of doubt is removed. May you then, O folks of dear Basra, be rewarded with the reward of Him who guides out of perplexity." Then there remained none among the people who did not rejoice at his joy, and they doled out to him whatever each had at hand. He accepted the bestowed bounty, and thanked them, then descended from the stone and walked towards the river bank. I followed in his wake, to where we found ourselves safe and alone together. Then I said to him: "This time you have done marvels, but what is your view as to repentance?"

He said: "I swear by Him who knows all hidden things, and forgives transgressions, my case is indeed a miracle and the prayers of my fellow people have been answered." I asked: "Enlighten me, please, so may Allah grant you more welfare!"

Said he: "Truly, I have stood before them in the stead of a doubter, a deceiver, and lo, I have turned from them with the heart of the devout, the contrite. Weal to them on whom they incline their hearts, and woe to him on whom they call down their imprecations."

Thereupon he bade me farewell, and turned away, leaving me in unrest, so that I did not cease to torment my thoughts on his account, and looking out for means of testing what he had stated. But every time I sniffed for tidings from wayfarers and roamers in foreign lands, I was like one who talked to dumb brutes, or hails a mute rock, until after a length of time and having reached the pitch of anguish, I met with some travellers returning from a journey, to whom I said: "Is there any rare news?" and they answered: "Indeed, we

have news rarer than the fabulous bird, the Anka." So
I asked them for an explanation, and they said that
they would mete out to me what had been meted out to
them. Then they told me that they had made a halt at
Seruj, after the wild asses had left it, and had seen there
its renowned Abu Zayd, who had donned the wool
cloak, and was leading the rows of the praying and had
become a famous devotee. Said I: "Do you mean him
of the Assemblies?" and they said "Yes, him, of all the
miraculous endowments."

Then longing for him returned, and I saw in him an
opportunity not to be lost. So I set out and made for
him in full earnestness, until I alighted at his mosque
and the place of his worship. He stood upright in his
prayer-niche, wearing a cloak stitched together with a
tooth-pick, and a patched wrapper. So I was struck
with awe of him, like one who has broken in upon
lions, and found him amongst those whose token is the
trace of prostration in their face, and when he had told
his rosary, he greeted me with his forefinger without
uttering a word of talk, nor asking for tidings old or
new. Then he proceeded with his recitation from the
Koran, and left me wondering at his devotion, and
envying them whom Allah leads aright amongst His
servants, and he did not desist from adoration and
humiliation, from prostrating himself and bowing
down, from self-abasement and contrition, until he had
completed the performance of the five prayers, and
today had become yesterday. Then he took me to his
abode, and gave me a share of his loaf and olive-oil.
Then he rose to enter his oratory, and remained alone
in converse with his Lord, until, when the morn shone
forth, and the wakeful worshipper was entitled to his
reward, he followed up his vigil with prayers of praise.
Then he reclined in the posture of the seeker of repose,
and began to chant with an impressive voice:

"Goodbye, my soul, to memories
   of vernal camps and tryst therein,

And fond farewell to traveller fair, yes, bid goodbye
to them for aye.
Bewail the time that passed away, when you have
blackened bright pages,
And never ceased to steep yourself in deeds of
shame and heinousness.
How often you spent the night in sins that none
before had dared,
From lust, indulged without restraint on wanton
couch, in chamber still,
How often sped upon your way to unheard-of
depravity;
And broken repentance, slowly vowed, in swift
forgetting sport and play;
How often you were bold, O slave, against the Lord
of heavens bright,
Not heeding Him and proving false, yes, false to
your pretended faith;
How often did you fling, like shoe outworn, aside His
sternest command,
Ungrateful for His benefits, and reckless of His
tardy wrath.
How often, seeking pleasure's couch, and glibly
speaking lies
You were neglecting the duties of His covenant.
So don the garb of penitence, and shower tears of
blood,
Before your foot commits the fatal slip, before your
fall has come to pass.
Humbly confess your sins and fly for refuge where
the guilty flies;
Resist your lewd propensities and turn from them
with firm purpose,
How long in thoughtlessness and sloth will you let
drift life's better part,
To what brings loss as only gain, and never check
your mad career.

Do you not perceive the mingled hue that streaks
with hoary lines your head,
Yet he whose ringlets blend with grey is warned of
his approaching death.
Woe then, my soul, redemption seek, obey, be true,
be well advised,
Take warning from those gone before, in generations
passed away,
And fear the stealing on of fate, be wary, lest you be
deceived
Walk in the path of rectitude, for swift, remember,
comes your doom,
Tomorrow will be your dwelling place in the bottom
of a lonely grave.
Alas, that house of sore dismay, that station, waste,
disconsolate,
That goal of pilgrims of long ago, of countless
pilgrims yet to come;
A house whose inmate will be seen, encompassed,
after ample space,
With the bond of cubits three, to hold him in their
narrow grip.
Who there alights, it matters not if he be wit or fool,
if poor, possessed of all the riches of a king;
And after it the roll-call comes, that musters timid
wight, and bold, and teacher, and disciple, and the
ruler and the ruled alike.
Then O the bliss of him that fears his Lord, and
earns the thrall's reward,
Safe from the dread account and from the terrors of
that awful day.
But O the loss of those who have sinned and trans-
gressed beyond all bounds,
And kindled discord's blazing fire, for sake of
worldly goods and joys.
O Thou, in whom my trust is placed, how grows my
fear with every day,
For all the slips and falls that fill my ill-spent life
with guilt and crime.

But, Lord, forgive Thy erring slave, yield mercy to his welling tears,
For the Most Merciful are You, and Best to Whom our prayers are raised."

Then, he did not stop repeating these words, in a low voice, and mingling them with sobs and sighs, until I wept too, as I had wept before on account of him.

Then he went to his mosque, cleansed by his night-watch, and I went behind in his tracks, and prayed with those who prayed behind him, and when the people dispersed and separated, he took to murmuring his lesson. I saw then that he had joined the Seven Saints, and that his heart was imbued with love of seclusion. So I decided to depart, and leave him by himself in this state.

Then it was as if he had read my purpose, or had revealed to him that which I kept concealed, for he sighed heavily and said: "If you make a resolution, put your trust in Allah."

So I went near to him and put my hand in his and said: "Give me your bequest, O servant of sincere counsel!" and he said "Keep death before your eyes, and this is the parting between you and me."

With this we said farewell, and the tears streamed from the corners of his eyes, and my sighs rose from within me, this being the last of our meetings.

For More Information about Sufism,
and to be on our mailing list, write:
Sufi Studies
P.O. Box 43
Los Altos, CA 94023
or go to the web at http://www.sufis.org